THE ELECTRONIC THEORY
OF ACIDS AND BASES

The
ELECTRONIC THEORY
of
ACIDS *and* BASES

BY

W. F. LUDER
Professor of Chemistry
Northeastern University

AND

SAVERIO ZUFFANTI
Professor of Chemistry
Northeastern University

SECOND REVISED EDITION

DOVER PUBLICATIONS, INC.

NEW YORK

Library of Congress Catalog Card Number: 61-19612

Manufactured in the United States of America

Dover Publications, Inc.
180 Varick Street
New York 14, N.Y.

To
GILBERT NEWTON LEWIS

PREFACE TO DOVER EDITION

While thinking about a revision of this book we vaguely anticipated having to make some sweeping changes in light of the large amount of related research which has transpired since the first edition of *The Electronic Theory of Acids and Bases* appeared in 1946. However, when we began the actual revision we were pleasantly surprised to discover that few changes were necessary. Practically all the new research supports the first edition without supplying many examples more convincing than those already used. Therefore only a few changes have been made and only a few additional examples and references have been added to this edition.

The second chapter has been revised more than the others. The atomic structure chart (p. 24) has been revised to make it correspond more closely with the energy-level diagram (also revised) on p. 22. On both charts the slanting lines represent successive main shells in the atoms. This representation makes the atomic structure chart reflect the energy relationships shown on the energy-level diagram and, at the same time, preserves the periods evident in other periodic tables. To illustrate this statement one may consider the difference between the slanting and horizontal rows as follows:

Because the differentiating electron for Ca (No. 20) is the second in the *fourth shell*, Ca is placed in the second column and in the *fourth slanting row*. But the differentiating electron for Sc (No. 21) is the ninth in the *third shell*, and therefore Sc is placed in the *third slanting row*. From Sc to Zn the differentiating electron is in the *third shell*, and the elements are placed in the *third slanting row*. The differentiating electron in Ga is the third in the *fourth shell*, and Ga is placed in the *fourth slanting row*. Ca and Ga are adjacent in the *fourth slanting row* although their atomic numbers are 20 and 31 respectively. Similar breaks occur between Sr and In and between Ba and Tl; a somewhat different one occurs between La and Hf (Nos. 57 and 72). These breaks correspond with the order in which sub-shells are completed according to the energy-level diagram.

As just described, the large numbers down the left side of the chart represent the *main shells* of the atoms when one refers to the *slanting rows*. The same numbers represent the *periods* of the elements if the elements are counted in *horizontal* rows. For example, the fourth period, of 18 elements, is counted from 19 and 20 straight across the horizontal gap to 21, through 30, then down to 31, and on to 36.

W. F. LUDER
SAVERIO ZUFFANTI

NORTHEASTERN UNIVERSITY
BOSTON, MASSACHUSETTS
January, 1961

PREFACE TO FIRST EDITION

The theory of relativity in physics has led to an increased amount of correlation in physical phenomena and to a keener insight into the fundamental problems of physics. More recently, another kind of relativity theory has made its appearance in chemistry. We owe this theory to the brilliant intuition of G. N. Lewis, by whom it was first proposed in 1923. Unfortunately, it was largely overlooked until about 1940. Since then, numerous papers have been published supporting and developing the theory, which is becoming known as the electronic theory of acids and bases.

According to the Lewis theory, acidity and basicity have nothing to do with the presence of any one element or specific group of elements. Nor is any particular substance to be considered an acid or a base in an absolute sense. Acidity and basicity are relative terms indicating certain types of experimental behavior which may be exhibited by the vast majority of chemical compounds. Most of them may behave either as acids or as bases depending upon conditions.

This theory makes possible a great increase in the amount of correlation possible in all phases of chemistry. It casts a flood of illumination over a wide area of apparently unrelated phenomena, from the corrosion of metals to catalysis in organic chemistry. In making such a statement, no claim of finality for the electronic theory of acids and bases is intended. No doubt the theory will be modified and improved. Nevertheless it seems evident that it can perform a useful function in chemistry. What this function is we hope to set forth more definitely in our conclusion (Chapter 13).

This book attempts a systematic presentation of the relationship of the electronic theory of acids and bases to chemistry as a whole. Much of the material has been published by us previously, in a series of papers in the *Journal of the American Chemical Society*, the *Journal of Chemical Education*, and *Chemical Reviews*. These papers have aroused so much interest that we have been encouraged to reorganize and combine them with some new material to make this book.

We have tried to present the electronic theory of acids and bases and its ramifications in an elementary manner. The theory is of interest to all types of chemists, and the book has been written with that in mind. Three chapters (10, 11, and 12) contain details on catalysis which are of most interest to organic chemists, but if necessary they can be skipped without losing continuity; Chapter 9 gives the essence of their contents.

One test of any new theory is: Does it offer a usable explanation which succeeds in correlating a larger number of experimental facts? We believe that according to this test the Lewis theory of acids and bases is successful. It does correlate a much larger body of experimental facts. On the other hand, a new theory in order to be convincing must not depart too far from previously accepted ideas. The wide interest in the Lewis theory indicates that it does not.

At the present time, then, the electronic theory of acids and bases seems to be the most satisfactory available. This is not to say that it is a final explanation. Like any other scientific theory, it is not to be believed in, but merely to be used until a more inclusive theory appears.

In conclusion, we express our gratitude to Professor G. Albert Hill for reading our manuscript and for his advice and encouragement, to Miss Amy F. Meserve for her assistance in the preparation of the manuscript, to Dean William C. White for his interest, and to the editors of the *Journal of Chemical Education*, the *Journal of the American Chemical Society*, and *Chemical Reviews* for their permission to use material first published in their journals.

We wish especially to acknowledge our great debt to Gilbert Newton Lewis, who shortly before his death read our manuscript and not only gave us the benefit of his suggestions and criticisms but granted us the privilege of dedicating our book to him.

W. F. LUDER
SAVERIO ZUFFANTI

NORTHEASTERN UNIVERSITY
BOSTON, MASSACHUSETTS
June, 1946

CONTENTS

Chapter 1

HISTORICAL BACKGROUND

1. Introduction.

The fundamental nature of acids and bases has been an intriguing problem for chemists since the time of Robert Boyle. The answer to the problem has been revised many times and is still the subject of considerable controversy. At present, there are no less than five competing theories of acids and bases! They may be listed as follows:

1. The water theory (sometimes called the Arrhenius theory).
2. The theory of solvent systems (Franklin-Germann).
3. The proton theory (Brønsted-Lowry).
4. The positive-negative theory (Usanovich).
5. The electronic theory (G. N. Lewis).

The most familiar of the five probably are the first three. The water theory of acids and bases was very widely accepted early in the century, though perhaps not so generally as we are inclined to think. For example, some organic chemists recognized substances like pyridine to be bases regardless of solvent, and the metallurgists spoke of acidic and basic linings for refining processes. More recently the proton theory of acids and bases has been gaining adherents rapidly, while a few chemists have preferred the theory of solvent systems.

But the fact is that none of these three theories satisfactorily explains more than a limited portion of the experimental behavior of acids and bases. For a long time an increasing amount of data has compelled realization of the fact that acid-base phenomena are far more widespread than is generally acknowledged. Those who have grasped this fact have already abandoned the water

1

theory. Yet neither the theory of solvent systems nor the proton theory is inclusive enough to cover all the data.

The theory of solvent systems conforms to the experimental fact that there are many other substances besides those containing hydrogen which exhibit typical acid properties. But it makes the definitions of acid and base as rigidly dependent upon the solvent as does the water theory.

The proton theory emphasizes the important fact that acid-base phenomena can be observed in any solvent or even in the absence of a solvent. It also takes into account the experimental fact that there are many other substances besides the hydroxide ion which exhibit typical basic properties. Yet it does not recognize the complementary data with regard to acids. The followers of Brønsted have maintained that only substances capable of giving up protons can be called acids.

We have, then, two independent and, in important features, contradictory theories of acids and bases. This situation seems to be due to the neglect of two factors: first, a portion of the experimental data, and second, the electronic theory of the covalent bond. Probably such neglect was natural and even necessary in the early stages of the development of each theory. Possibly neither would have accomplished as much as it has without some such limitation. However, as a result of this neglect, neither theory gives an insight into the fundamental nature of acids and bases.

One of the most powerful theoretical tools available to the chemist is the electronic theory of the covalent bond, which we owe primarily to G. N. Lewis. Lewis was also the first to suggest an electronic explanation of acid-base phenomena.[1] The theory of the covalent bond is now almost universally accepted among chemists, but the electronic theory of acids and bases until quite recently has been ignored where it has not been actively opposed.[2]

Lewis's definitions of acids and bases do not depend upon the presence of any particular element. As he himself points out: "To restrict the group of acids to those substances which contain hydrogen interferes as seriously with the systematic understanding of chemistry as would the restriction of the term oxidizing

[1] Lewis, *Valence and the Structure of Atoms and Molecules*, Chemical Catalog Company, New York, 1923.

[2] Walden, *Salts, Acids, and Bases*, McGraw-Hill Book Company, New York, 1929.

agent to substances containing oxygen." [3] Another theory which starts from the same point is that of Usanovich, which will be considered below.

From an experimental standpoint, a substance that exhibits the properties of an acid should be called an acid, regardless of preconceived notions about the dependence of acidic properties on a particular element. Those properties have been agreed upon from the beginning. Yet many substances possessing them are not yet generally recognized as acids. This situation persists in spite of the fact that some of these substances were once called acids, when the principal criterion of an acid was its experimental behavior.

Some of the properties by which acids were recognized when the term first came into use were listed by Boyle [2] as follows: they dissolve many substances; they precipitate sulfur from its solution in alkalies; they change blue plant dyes to red; they lose all these properties on contact with alkalies. These were recognized as the properties of aqueous solutions of acids. If the solution of a substance in water had these and other typical acid properties, the substance itself was known as an acid. Thus carbon dioxide and sulfur trioxide were called acids because their solutions exhibited the properties common to all aqueous solutions of acids.

This strictly experimental approach was largely abandoned during the series of controversies which began with Lavoisier's attempt to make oxygen the necessary constituent of all acids. After Davy had shown that some acids do not contain oxygen, hydrogen became the "acidifying principle." Davy himself wrote in 1814 that "Acidity does not depend upon any particular elementary substance, but upon peculiar arrangement of various substances." [4] We shall see how nearly correct Davy was. But Liebig successfully maintained the hydrogen theory against Berzelius by defining an acid as any substance that contains easily replaceable hydrogen atoms.

With the advent of the Arrhenius theory of ionization, an acid was defined as a hydrogen compound ionizing in water solution to give hydrogen ions. A base was a hydroxyl compound which would give hydroxide ions in water solution. The reaction between an acid and a base—i.e., neutralization—would produce a salt and water:

$$HA + BOH \rightarrow BA + H_2O$$

acid   base   salt   water

[3] Lewis, *J. Franklin Inst.*, **226**, 293 (1938).
[4] Hall, *J. Chem. Education*, **17**, 124 (1940).

These definitions were quite generally adopted in spite of the efforts of several investigators to show how inadequate they were. The emphasis upon ions in chemical reactions was at its height. A physical chemistry textbook of the period, as quoted by Folin and Flanders,[5] contained the statement, "We have already reached a point where we can say that nearly all, if not all, chemical reactions are due to ions, molecules as such not entering into chemical action." In this atmosphere the work of Collie and Tickle,[6] Hantzsch,[7] Folin and Flanders,[5] and Lapworth [8] was largely overlooked.

Collie and Tickle,[6] in their paper published in 1899, suggested that oxonium salts are similar to ammonium salts. They referred to "such bases as those of the pyridine series" and even spoke of the "hypothetical base oxonium hydroxide, OH_3OH." Hantzsch noted the basic action of water, methyl alcohol, and dimethyl ether in anhydrous sulfuric acid. Folin and Flanders, in a paper published in 1912,[5] reported the titration of a large number of acids in such solvents as benzene, toluene, chloroform, and carbon tetrachloride. They used sodium ethoxide and sodium amoxide as bases and phenolphthalein as an indicator. They noted that weak acids which cannot be titrated in water give excellent results in organic solvents. Even hydrogen sulfide was titrated. They found their solutions of acids practically non-conducting and concluded that very few ions were present. (This conclusion has been supported by the work of Fuoss and Kraus.[9]) Carbon dioxide could not be titrated in either chloroform or benzene, a result which seems to agree with Lewis's statement that carbon dioxide is a "secondary" acid (Chapter 3). The most striking thing about their paper appears in a footnote in which the authors mention that mercuric chloride can be titrated with phenolphthalein and sodium ethoxide in the same manner as any other acid, but they failed to draw the logical conclusion that mercuric chloride might be an acid. Lapworth was one of the first to attack the Arrhenius-

[5] Folin and Flanders, J. Am. Chem. Soc., **34,** 774 (1912).

[6] Collie and Tickle, J. Chem. Soc., **75,** 710 (1899).

[7] Hantzsch, Z. physik. Chem., **61,** 257 (1908); Hantzsch, ibid., **65,** 41 (1909); Hantzsch, Z. Electrochem., **24,** 201 (1918); Hantzsch, ibid., **29,** 221 (1923).

[8] Lapworth, J. Chem. Soc., **107,** 857 (1915).

[9] Fuoss and Kraus, J. Am. Chem. Soc., **55,** 2387 (1933); Fuoss and Kraus, ibid., **55,** 3614 (1933); Luder, P. B. Kraus, C. A. Kraus, and Fuoss, ibid., **58,** 255 (1936).

Ostwald theory of the catalytic activity of acids. However, these and similar investigations failed to make much impression until the concept of the covalent bond began to reduce the overemphasis upon ionic reactions.

With the growing clarity of the electronic theory of valence, the inadequacy of the water theory of acids and bases was increasingly recognized. Even more important was the large amount of work undertaken with solvents other than water. It soon became evident that acid-base phenomena could also be observed in non-aqueous solvents. Many non-aqueous solvents are incapable of ionizing as water does, and many of the so-called organic bases are also non-ionic, e.g., pyridine. Even when ions are produced in non-aqueous solvents by the reaction of compounds that had gradually come to be recognized as bases, the anion, of course, is not the hydroxide ion. Two alternatives seemed available: (1) to make the definitions independent of solvent, but to retain hydrogen as the one essential element; or (2) to make the definitions independent of any particular element, but to tie them very closely to the solvent in which the phenomena were observed. We shall consider the proton theory first.

2. One-Element Theories of Acids and Bases.

Before discussion of the Brønsted-Lowry theory a few words about an earlier one-element theory may not be amiss. The first one-element theory was apparently due to Lavoisier. Oxygen was supposed to be necessary for the manifestation of acidic properties. Later it became evident that some substances that do not contain oxygen are nevertheless acids. Instead of concluding with Davy that no particular element is responsible for acidity, most chemists of the time, in spite of the opposition of Berzelius, gradually swung over to the view that hydrogen was essential to an acid. Now, one hundred years later, we find ourselves in the same position of having to give up an element, except that it is hydrogen we must give up instead of oxygen.

In spite of the overwhelming trend toward hydrogen as the "acidifying principle," some remnants of the theory of Berzelius persisted—for example, the use by metallurgists of the term "acid" to denote oxides such as silicon dioxide and the term "base" for oxides like calcium oxide. Berzelius, as a consequence of his theory of valence, classified oxides as acids or bases. Furthermore, the theory provided a method of predicting the relative strengths of acids or bases.[10] Bases like sodium oxide were supposed to be strong because of the high positive charge on the metal of the combination. The negative charge in oxides was supposed to be due to oxygen, and the acidity of acids was due to the high negative charge of the oxygen compared to the weaker positive charge of the non-metallic constituent, such as sulfur or carbon. Therefore, acids with a high proportion of oxygen should be strong. For example, sulfur trioxide should be a stronger acid than sulfur dioxide. This prediction is in accord with the experimental facts, as we shall see later, but development along this line was halted because of the inadequacy of the theory of valence upon which it depended.

When Berzelius' theory of valence was discarded, primarily as the result of Faraday's discovery of the laws of electrolysis, the theory of acids and bases founded upon it also had to be abandoned. Doubt had already been cast on it by Davy's demonstration that hydrochloric acid did not contain oxygen. There was no doubt of the acidity of hydrochloric acid; so, still thinking in terms of an elementary acidifying principle, many chemists came to regard hydrogen as the one element necessary for acid properties. Ideas regarding bases did not become so definite until the advent of the proton-donor theory.

The modern one-element theory of acids and bases is usually credited to Brønsted and Lowry. They proposed the proton theory independently in 1923. But G. N. Lewis, who set forth his electronic definitions of acids and bases in the same year, also explained the proton-donor concept as a special case of his broader theory.[1] According to the proton theory, an acid donates a proton to a base, and a base accepts a proton from an acid. The acid and base may be either compounds or ions, as shown in the following examples:

$$\text{HCl} + \overset{\smile}{\text{N}}\text{H}_3 \rightarrow \text{Cl}^{-1} + \text{NH}_4{}^{+1}$$
$$\text{\small acid} \qquad \text{\small base}$$

$$\text{NH}_4{}^{+1} + \overset{\smile}{\text{O}}\text{H}^{-1} \rightarrow \text{NH}_3 + \text{H}_2\text{O}$$
$$\text{\small acid} \qquad \text{\small base}$$

This picture of acid-base reactions makes them independent of solvent, as is shown in the first equation, and eliminates the arti-

[10] Palmer, *Valency: Classical and Modern*, Cambridge University Press, Cambridge, England, 1944.

ficial connection between acids, bases, and salts, as is shown in the second equation.

Since any group of atoms that gives up a proton is called an acid, acids may be cations, anions, or neutral molecules:

$$NH_4^{+1} + C_2H_3O_2^{-1} \rightarrow HC_2H_3O_2 + NH_3$$

$$HSO_4^{-1} + OH^{-1} \rightarrow HOH + SO_4^{-2}$$

$$\underset{\text{acid}}{HCl} + \underset{\text{base}}{C_5H_5N} \rightarrow C_5H_5NH^{+1} + Cl^{-1}$$

Bases also may be cations, anions, or molecules:

$$Co(OH)(NH_3)_5^{+2} + H_3O^{+1} \rightarrow Co(H_2O)(NH_3)_5^{+3} + H_2O$$

$$C_2H_3O_2^{-1} + H_2O \rightarrow HC_2H_3O_2 + OH^{-1}$$

$$\underset{\text{base}}{C_2H_5OH} + \underset{\text{acid}}{HCl} \rightarrow C_2H_5OH_2^{+1} + Cl^{-1}$$

When an acid gives up its proton, the residue must be a base, since it can retrieve a proton. The acid and base thus related are called a conjugate system:

$$\underset{\text{acid}_1}{NH_4^{+1}} \rightleftarrows \underset{\text{base}_1}{NH_3} + H^{+1}$$

This equation does not represent an actual reaction, since none takes place unless a base is present to accept the proton, e.g.:

$$H^+ + \underset{\text{base}_2}{OH^{-1}} \rightarrow \underset{\text{acid}_2}{H_2O}$$

Addition of these two equations gives

$$\underset{\text{acid}_1}{NH_4^{+1}} + \underset{\text{base}_2}{OH^{-1}} \rightleftarrows \underset{\text{acid}_2}{HOH} + \underset{\text{base}_1}{NH_3}$$

The reaction involves two conjugate pairs. Probably the most direct way of describing what happens in such a reaction is to say that the two bases (NH_3 and OH^{-1}) are competing for the proton.

When we consider the familiar types of acid-base phenomena, such as ionization and hydrolysis, we find them all described by the type equation

$$\text{acid}_1 + \text{base}_2 \rightarrow \text{base}_1 + \text{acid}_2$$

as shown in the following equations:

Ionization:

$$\text{HCl} + \text{H}_2\text{O} \rightarrow \text{H}_3\text{O}^{+1} + \text{Cl}^{-1}$$
strong acid in water

$$\text{HC}_2\text{H}_3\text{O}_2 + \text{H}_2\text{O} \rightleftarrows \text{H}_3\text{O}^{+1} + \text{C}_2\text{H}_3\text{O}_2^{-1}$$
weak acid in water

$$\text{HOH} + \text{NH}_3 \rightleftarrows \text{NH}_4^{+1} + \text{OH}^{-1}$$
weak base in water

$$\text{HCl} + \text{C}_2\text{H}_5\text{OH} \rightleftarrows \text{C}_2\text{H}_5\text{OH}_2^{+1} + \text{Cl}^{-1}$$
HCl in alcohol

Hydrolysis:

$$\text{H}_2\text{O} + \text{C}_2\text{H}_3\text{O}_2^{-1} \rightleftarrows \text{HC}_2\text{H}_3\text{O}_2 + \text{OH}^{-1}$$
hydrolysis of sodium acetate

$$\text{NH}_4^{+1} + \text{H}_2\text{O} \rightleftarrows \text{H}_3\text{O}^{+1} + \text{NH}_3$$
hydrolysis of ammonium chloride

One method of comparing the strengths of acids and bases is by means of the equilibrium constant. For example, for molecular acids (such as $\text{HC}_2\text{H}_3\text{O}_2$) in water, the equation reduces to an expression equivalent to that of the water theory:

$$\text{HC}_2\text{H}_3\text{O}_2 + \text{H}_2\text{O} \rightleftarrows \text{H}_3\text{O}^{+1} + \text{C}_2\text{H}_3\text{O}_2^{-1}$$

$$K' = \frac{[\text{H}_3\text{O}^{+1}] \times [\text{C}_2\text{H}_3\text{O}_2^{-1}]}{[\text{HC}_2\text{H}_3\text{O}_2] \times [\text{H}_2\text{O}]}$$

$$K = K' \times [\text{H}_2\text{O}] = \frac{[\text{H}_3\text{O}^{+1}] \times [\text{C}_2\text{H}_3\text{O}_2^{-1}]}{[\text{HC}_2\text{H}_3\text{O}_2]}$$

The equation gives the strength of the acid relative to H_3O^{+1}. For a cation acid such as the ammonium ion, the equilibrium constant is seen to be identical with what was previously called the hydrolysis constant:

$$\text{NH}_4^{+1} + \text{H}_2\text{O} \rightleftarrows \text{H}_3\text{O}^{+1} + \text{NH}_3$$

$$K = \frac{[\text{H}_3\text{O}^{+1}] \times [\text{NH}_3]}{[\text{NH}_4^{+1}]}$$

A strong acid (HCl) must have a weak conjugate base (Cl^{-1}); conversely, a weak acid ($HC_2H_3O_2$) must have a strong conjugate base ($C_2H_3O_2^{-1}$). The relationship between an acid and its conjugate base makes it unnecessary to list basic dissociation constants. For example, for ammonia

$$K_b = \frac{[NH_4^{+1}] \times [OH^{-1}]}{[NH_3]}$$

but

$$K_b = \frac{[NH_4^{+1}] \times [OH^{-1}]}{[NH_3]} \times \frac{K_w}{[H_3O^{+1}] \times [OH^{-1}]}$$

$$= \frac{K_w[NH_4^{+1}]}{[H_3O^{+1}] \times [NH_3]} = \frac{K_w}{K_a}$$

where K_a refers to the ammonium ion.

This method of comparing the strengths of acids according to the extent of reaction with the solvent cannot be used for all solvents. If the solvent is inert, e.g., a hydrocarbon, other methods must be adopted. Some of them will be discussed later.

The proton theory of acids and bases recognizes the existence of a large number and variety of bases, both molecular and ionic: hydroxide ion, amide ion, ethoxide ion, piperidine and other amines, alcohols, ethers, acetate ion, hydrosulfide ion, cyanide ion, bisulfate ion, ketones, and many others. It also recognizes that acid-base phenomena do not depend upon the solvent. But its great weakness is that it ignores a large body of experimental data by restricting the use of the word *acid* to proton donors. For a time the only alternative to the proton theory seemed to be the theory of solvent systems.

3. The Theory of Solvent Systems.

The development of the theory of solvent systems was begun by Franklin in 1905.[11] Reasoning from formal analogy to the hydrogen ion-hydroxide ion theory he defined acids and bases in liquid ammonia. According to his theory, if water ionizes into hydronium and hydroxide ions, liquid ammonia must ionize into ammonium and amide ions:

$$2H_2O \rightleftarrows H_3O^{+1} + OH^{-1}$$
$$2NH_3 \rightleftarrows NH_4^{+1} + NH_2^{-1}$$

[11] Franklin, *J. Am. Chem. Soc.*, **27**, 820 (1905).

Substances like ammonium chloride are acids, and substances like sodium amide are bases, in liquid ammonia. Ammonia solutions of acids and bases neutralize each other just as aqueous solutions do. For example:

$$OH_3Cl + NaOH \rightarrow NaCl + 2H_2O$$

$$\underset{\text{acid}}{NH_4Cl} + \underset{\text{base}}{NaNH_2} \rightarrow \underset{\text{salt}}{NaCl} + \underset{\text{solvent}}{2NH_3}$$

Other characteristic properties of acids and bases, such as the reaction of acids with metals and of bases with non-metals, were observed. The similarity between ammonia and water solutions was demonstrated very widely.[12] Acids like $B(OH)_3$ and $B(NH_2)_3$ were compared, and the latter was called an ammono acid. BiN reacts with NH_4I in ammonia to form BiI_3 and NH_3, just as in water Bi_2O_3 reacts with HCl to give $BiCl_3$ and H_2O. The behavior of Zn $(NH_2)_2$ in ammonia is analogous to that of $Zn(OH)_2$ in water. Both are insoluble, but the addition of KNH_2 and KOH, respectively, brings them into solution. $Zn(NH_2)_2$ is amphoteric in the same way that $Zn(OH)_2$ is:

$$Zn(OH)_2 + 2OH^{-1} \rightarrow Zn(OH)_4^{-2}$$

$$Zn(NH_2)_2 + 2NH_2^{-1} \rightarrow Zn(NH_2)_4^{-2}$$

Since metals evolve hydrogen when reacting with either hydronium ions in water or ammonium ions in ammonia,

$$2H_3O^{+1} + Mg \rightarrow Mg^{+2} + 2H_2O + H_2$$

$$2NH_4^{+1} + Mg \rightarrow Mg^{+2} + 2NH_3 + H_2$$

it appeared that the acid properties of both the hydronium and the ammonium ions must be due to the proton. The question then arose whether the idea of the solvent system could be applied to systems in which no protons were present.

Germann, Cady and Elsey, Jander, Wickert, and Smith have extended the solvent system theory of acids and bases to include non-protonic systems. Germann[13] showed that aluminum chloride in phosgene has typical acid properties. The solution dissolves metals with evolution of carbon monoxide gas and is neutralized

[12] Franklin, *Am. Chem. J.*, **47**, 285 (1912); Franklin, *J. Am. Chem. Soc.*, **46**, 2137 (1924); Franklin, *The Nitrogen System of Compounds*, Reinhold Publishing Corporation, New York, 1935.

[13] Germann and Timpany, *J. Am. Chem. Soc.*, **47**, 2275 (1925); Germann, *ibid.*, **47**, 2461 (1925); *Science*, **61**, 70 (1925).

by metallic chlorides such as calcium chloride. Germann assumed that the aluminum chloride forms with the solvent a complex which he called a solvo acid:

$$COCl_2 \rightleftarrows COCl^{+1} + Cl^{-1}$$
$$\text{ionization of the solvent}$$

$$AlCl_3 + COCl_2 \rightleftarrows COCl^{+1} + AlCl_4^{-1}$$

The concentration of the solvent cations has been increased by the addition of the acid (aluminum chloride); hence the reaction of the solution with a metal is more rapid than that of the solvent alone:

$$Ca + COCl^{+1} \rightarrow Ca^{+2} + CO + Cl^{-1}$$

This is analogous to the reaction in water: [14]

$$Ca + 2H^{+1} \rightarrow Ca^{+2} + H_2$$

Germann's definitions of acids and bases were simplified by Cady and Elsey,[15] who defined an acid as a solute that gives rise to a cation characteristic of the solvent, and a base as a solute that gives rise to an anion characteristic of the solvent.

Jander[16] and coworkers used these last definitions to interpret the results of their work with liquid sulfur dioxide as solvent. Thionyl chloride is acidic, tetramethylammonium sulfite is basic, and aluminum sulfite is amphoteric in liquid sulfur dioxide. Ionization of this solvent gives thionyl and sulfite ions:

$$2SO_2 \rightleftarrows SO^{+2} + SO_3^{-2}$$

The neutralization of thionyl chloride by tetramethylammonium sulfite in this solvent is represented as follows (assuming that neutralization is the formation of salt and solvent):

$$SOCl_2 + [(CH_3)_4N]_2SO_3 \rightarrow 2(CH_3)_4NCl + 2SO_2$$
$$\text{acid} \qquad \text{base} \qquad\qquad\quad \text{salt} \qquad \text{solvent}$$

The amphoteric behavior of $Al_2(SO_3)_3$ in sulfur dioxide is analogous to that of $Al(OH)_3$ in water. Each contains the negative ion of the respective solvent. Aluminum sulfite, which is insoluble in sulfur dioxide, dissolves on addition of either thionyl chloride

---

[14] No doubt both positive ions (H^{+1} and $COCl^{+1}$) are solvated, but we assume this to be understood. Therefore we shall indicate this solvation only when showing it is necessary for clarity in our discussion.

[15] Cady and Elsey, *J. Chem. Education*, **5**, 1425 (1928).

[16] Jander and Mesech, *Z. physik. Chem.*, **A183**, 255 (1939); also see preceding papers in this series.

or tetramethylammonium sulfite, just as aluminum hydroxide, which is insoluble in water, dissolves on addition of either nitric acid or potassium hydroxide.

Smith [17] changed the definitions somewhat in reviewing his work with selenium oxychloride as a solvent. He found that stannic, ferric, silicon, arsenious, and titanium chlorides and sulfur trioxide displayed typical acid properties in selenium oxychloride. He defined an acid as an electron-pair acceptor toward the solvent, and a base as an electron-pair donor toward the solvent. These definitions, suggested in 1938, were the first to show the influence of the proposals made by Lewis in 1923.

The height of formalism was reached by Wickert [18] in his definitions of acids and bases in terms of the solvent system. He overlooks such experimental behavior as amphoterism in order to state his definitions wholly in terms of ions. Shatenstein [19] also has pointed out one of the several inconsistencies in Wickert's presentation. Although Wickert defines an acid as an ionic compound the cation of which has an incomplete electronic configuration, he recognizes that ammonium salts are acids in ammonia. Another contradiction of the experimental facts is his listing of antimony trichloride but not aluminum chloride as an acid.

The essential ideas of the theory of solvent systems are summarized in Table 1. In the first three examples, it is obvious enough that the acid that has reacted with each solvent is hydrogen bromide. But Smith [17] seems to be the only adherent of the theory of solvent systems who recognized that in examples 5 and 6 aluminum chloride and stannic chloride are true acids.

TABLE 1

NEUTRALIZATION REACTIONS ACCORDING TO THE THEORY OF SOLVENT SYSTEMS

Solvent	Acid	+	Base	→	Salt	+	Solvent
H_2O	H_3O^{+1}, Br^{-1}		K^{+1}, OH^{-1}		K^{+1}, Br^{-1}		$2H_2O$
NH_3	NH_4^{+1}, Br^{-1}		K^{+1}, NH_2^{-1}		K^{+1}, Br^{-1}		$2NH_3$
C_2H_5OH	$C_2H_5OH_2^{+1}$, Br^{-1}		K^{+1}, $OC_2H_5^{-1}$		K^{+1}, Br^{-1}		$2C_2H_5OH$
SO_2	SO^{+2}, Br_2^{-1}		K_2^{+1}, SO_3^{-2}		$2K^{+1}$, Br^{-1}		$2SO_2$
$COCl_2$	$COCl^{+1}$, $AlCl_4^{-1}$		K^{+1}, Cl^{-1}		K^{+1}, $AlCl_4^{-1}$		$COCl_2$
$SeOCl_2$	$(SeOCl)_2^{+1}$, $SnCl_6^{-2}$		$2K^{+1}$, Cl^{-1}		K_2^{+1}, $SnCl_6^{-2}$		$2SeOCl_2$
$SbCl_3$	Sb^{+3}, Br_3^{-1}		$3K^{+1}$, Cl^{-1}		$3K^{+1}$, Br^{-1}		$SbCl_3$

[17] Smith, *Chem. Revs.*, **23**, 165 (1938).

[18] Wickert, *Z. physik. Chem.*, **A178**, 361 (1937).

[19] Shatenstein, *J. Gen. Chem. U.S.S.R.*, **9**, 1603 (1939).

The strength of the solvent-systems theory lies in its emphasis upon the fact that acid behavior is not confined to solutions containing proton donors. The advocates of the theory have demonstrated that, although their acid solutions do not contain protons, they show all the typical experimental behavior of aqueous solutions of hydrogen acids. The weaknesses of this theory are two: first, the limitation of acid-base phenomena to solvent systems; and second, the emphasis upon ionization as the most important factor in acid-base properties. Probably the first followed from the second; at any rate, many investigators [20] have shown that ionization plays a far less important role than is indicated by the solvent-systems theory. It would appear that this theory describes only one aspect of the nature of acids and bases: namely, their reactions with amphoteric solvents and the properties of the resulting solutions. We are most familiar with these properties since they are most easily observed. A reluctance to go beyond them is readily understood, but for many chemists the Brønsted theory has overcome this reluctance, at least with respect to bases. But the Brønsted theory admits of no acids other than proton donors. As the proponents of the solvent-systems theory have shown, this limitation does not correspond to the experimental facts. If the experimental approach is to prevail, it is improper to go on saying—as Meerwein,[21] Shatenstein,[19] and others do— that certain substances are "acid-analogous" because of their properties but are not acids because they do not contain hydrogen. Brønsted is undoubtedly correct in attributing acid-base properties to the molecules themselves rather than to their solutions. In this respect the Brønsted theory, as far as it goes, is closer to the experimental facts than the theory of solvent systems. Just as important is Brønsted's view that acids and bases are not necessarily ionic.

4. The Positive-Negative Theory.

Any attempt to reconcile these two contradictory theories of acids and bases must involve a deeper insight into their fundamental nature. One such attempt has been made by Usanovich.[22]

[20] See references 5–8; Hammett, *J. Am. Chem. Soc.*, **50**, 2666 (1928); Hammett, *Chem. Revs.*, **13**, 61 (1933); Hantzsch and Voigt, *Ber.*, **62B**, 970 (1929); LaMer and Downes, *Chem. Revs.*, **13**, 47 (1933); Wynne-Jones, *J. Chem. Soc.*, **1930**, 1064.

[21] Meerwein, *Ann.*, **455**, 227 (1927).

[22] Usanovich, *J. Gen. Chem. U.S.S.R.*, **9**, 182 (1939).

Usanovich has defined an acid as any substance capable of giving up cations or of combining with anions, and a base as any substance capable of giving up anions or of combining with cations. He also suggests that oxidation-reduction reactions are a special case of acid-base phenomena. Acids combine with electrons as well as with anions, and bases give up electrons to acids. Oxidizing power is a limited phase of acidity, and both are due to attraction for negative particles. Some examples of neutralization according to Usanovich are given in Table 2.

TABLE 2

NEUTRALIZATION REACTIONS ACCORDING TO THE THEORY OF USANOVICH

Acid	+	*Base*	→	*Salt*
SO_3		Na_2O		Na_2SO_4
Sb_2S_5		$3(NH_4)_2S$		$2(NH_4)_3SbS_4$
$Fe(CN)_3$		$3KCN$		$K_3Fe(CN)_6$
CH_3I		$(CH_3)_3N$		$(CH_3)_4NI$
Cl_2		$2Na$		$2NaCl$

Sulfur trioxide is an acid because it combines with the anion O^{-2}:

$$SO_3 + O^{-2} \rightarrow SO_4^{-2}$$

Antimony pentasulfide is an acid because it combines with the sulfide ion:

$$Sb_2S_5 + 3S^{-2} \rightarrow 2SbS_4^{-3}$$

Ferric cyanide combines with the cyanide ion. Methyl iodide gives up the cation CH_3^{+1}. Chlorine combines with two electrons from two sodium atoms.

This theory is general and covers more of the experimental behavior, but objections may be raised to it. Certain inconsistencies have been pointed out by Shatenstein,[19] among them the emphasis upon salt formation and the formal reasoning involved in making ions so important in the scheme. In addition, one might mention the lack of correlation between the definitions and the degree of "coordination-unsaturation" which Usanovich recognizes is of great importance in determining acidity and basicity. In one sense the positive-negative theory is a retrogression to the early ideas of Berzelius on valence. Furthermore, the inclusion of oxidation-reduction as a special case of acid-base phenomena does not seem to be justified. The relationship is close but, as we shall see, not quite as Usanovich presents it.

5. The Electronic Theory of Acids and Bases.

An earlier attempt to reconcile the proton and the solvent-systems theories was made by G. N. Lewis in 1923.[1] Strictly speaking, it was not an attempt at reconciliation, since both theories were proposed independently by Lewis as special cases of his more general and more fundamental theory. Brønsted and Lowry presented their ideas in the same year, but the *general* form of the solvent-systems theory came several years later. The conflict between the two theories has gone on, although the solution to the problem has been at hand since 1923. Each theory was consistent as far as it went, but each was merely part of the whole picture. The inclusion of both into one clear, simple, and fundamental theory was accomplished by Lewis largely because he founded his theory firmly upon experimental facts, allowing no preconceived notion of the necessity of a particular element or of the desirability of emphasizing ions or the solvent to interfere.

Lewis chose four familiar experimental criteria as the basis of his definitions of acids and bases. The four "phenomenological criteria" are:

I. *Neutralization.* Primary acids and bases may combine more or less rapidly with each other.

II. *Titration with Indicators.* Acids and bases may be titrated against each other by the use of substances, usually colored, known as indicators.

III. *Displacement.* An acid or base will in general replace a weaker acid or base from its compounds.

IV. *Catalysis.* Acids and bases frequently act as catalysts.

All four of these characteristics must be displayed by a particular substance for classification as an acid or a base. However, in order to make the definitions as concise as possible, the first and second properties, neutralization and titration with indicators, are chosen for specific mention. *Acids are substances which, like hydrogen chloride, neutralize sodium hydroxide or any other base. Bases are substances which, like sodium hydroxide, neutralize hydrogen chloride or any other acid.* Many substances are capable of acting in either way and are called *amphoteric.*

These definitions include both the Brønsted and the solvent-systems theories as well as the water theory. The list of bases according to the Lewis theory is identical with that according to the Brønsted theory, and all the substances recognized as acids by the solvent-systems theory are included. A simple experiment, first suggested by Lewis,[3] strikingly illustrates the application of these definitions. It is only one of many that can easily be performed (see Chapter 7). Crystal violet is an indicator which gives the same color change in different solvents. When sodium hydroxide is titrated against hydrochloric acid in water, with crystal violet as the indicator, the solution is yellow when strongly acidic and violet when basic. Pyridine and triethylamine can be titrated in a similar manner against hydrochloric acid and are therefore bases. If pyridine is dissolved in some comparatively inert solvent, such as chlorobenzene, the same violet color is observed when crystal violet is added. Now, if boron trichloride or stannic chloride is added to the basic pyridine solution, the color changes to yellow. Thus, boron trichloride and stannic chloride are acids. If triethylamine, acetone, or any other fairly strong base is added, the color changes back to violet. Similar titrations can be performed in other solvents with other indicators and with many other acids and bases none of which contains hydrogen or hydroxide ions. With the proper choice of solvent and indicator, all the substances that are acids according to the solvent-systems theory can be shown to be acids on this experimental basis (neutralization and titration). Displacement and catalysis reactions support this conclusion. Especially striking is the similarity in the action of acid catalysts such as aluminum and boron trichlorides, sulfur trioxide, hydrogen fluoride, and sulfuric acid. (Both displacement and catalysis will be considered in some detail in subsequent chapters.) All four of these experimental criteria provide ample evidence that there is an inherent difference between acids and bases. The difference is not dependent upon the solvent or upon the presence of a particular element. Therefore it would seem to involve a contrast in electronic configuration.

Searching for the property common to all acids, or that common to all bases, Lewis concluded that acids and bases correspond respectively to what Sidgwick later called acceptor and donor molecules.[23] Neutralization is the formation of the coordinate covalent bond [24] between the acid and the base. Such a definition

[23] Sidgwick, *The Electronic Theory of Valency*, Oxford University Press, New York, 1927.

[24] The coordinate covalent bond will be discussed in the next chapter.

holds when the acid and base are either hydrogen ion [25] and hydroxide ion

$$H^{+1} + :\overset{..}{\underset{..}{O}}:H^{-1} \rightarrow H:\overset{..}{\underset{..}{O}}:H$$

acid   base

or boron trichloride and ammonia

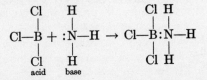

acid   base

The base donates a share in a lone pair of electrons to the acid to form the coordinate covalent bond between the two. Formation of the coordinate bond is always to be considered the first step, even though ionization may subsequently take place. Examples of ionization will be considered in later chapters.

Before discussing the consequences of these ideas further, let us now turn to a consideration of some of the more recent developments in the theory of valence inasmuch as the "rule of eight" in valence theory still has not been discarded by many chemists. For example, in order to understand why the covalent compound stannic chloride, a liquid much like carbon tetrachloride in physical properties, is such a strong acid, we must become familiar with the limitations of the octet theory. This can be accomplished without reference to any theory of acids and bases. The following chapter deals with the rule of two which replaces the rule of eight. It also contains suggestions for the modification in writing electronic formulas which must be made in adopting the newer ideas.

[25] In general we shall refer to the "hydronium ion" as the hydrogen ion and write its formula as H^{+1} wherever use of the formula H_3O^{+1} does not add to the discussion.

Chapter 2

ATOMIC ORBITALS AND VALENCE

1. Introduction.

One of the most powerful tools available to the chemist is the electronic theory of valence. Still it is not yet being used generally to full advantage. The two principal factors responsible for the delay seem to be reluctance to abandon the rule of eight and failure to make use of the concept of atomic orbitals.

Ever since the proposal of the theory of the covalent bond by G. N. Lewis in 1916, it has been obvious that there are numerous compounds which do not "obey" the rule of eight, which was strongly emphasized by Kossel and Langmuir. However, elementary textbooks have stressed it so thoroughly that the rule of eight is still generally accepted by those unfamiliar with the recent literature in the field.

The idea of atomic orbitals from elementary quantum theory is now often presented as an aid to the understanding of atomic structure but is still rarely applied to the problem of valence. It is the purpose of this chapter to show in an elementary way how abandoning the rule of eight and applying the theory of atomic orbitals can lead to fuller understanding of valence. In order to do this, some of the details, such as are involved in hybridization of orbits, for example, will be either omitted or modified for the sake of simplicity. Some of the modifications explicitly proposed or implicit in the discussion may give rise to objection on the ground that they do not give the complete picture. But, after all, we do not yet understand all the phenomena of valence by any means.

2. The Rule of Eight.

The familiar dictum that in forming chemical bonds atoms gain, lose, or share electrons to make the outermost shell of each atom contain eight electrons probably gained such general acceptance because the majority of known chemical compounds is made up primarily of elements in the first two rows of the periodic table. With but few exceptions, these elements do obey the rule of eight. The presence of carbon with its thousands of compounds seems to lend added support to the rule. Actually, of course, the sheer number of compounds of any one element has no bearing whatever on the rule of eight. The carbon atom counts merely as one atom in the ten. But, even in these ten, two of the eight elements which do not already have complete valence shells refuse to obey the rule of eight, namely, beryllium and boron.

There is little doubt that boron trichloride is a covalent compound and, therefore, that the boron atom in the compound has only six electrons in its valence shell (crosses represent original boron electrons):

Beryllium chloride also seems to be covalent, as shown by its high solubility in benzene. If the compound is covalent the beryllium atom has four outer electrons in beryllium chloride (the two crosses represent the two electrons from the beryllium atom):

$$:\overset{..}{Cl}_\times^\times Be_\times^\times \overset{..}{Cl}:$$

When the third period is considered, five out of seven atoms show "exceptions" to the rule of eight: aluminum, silicon, phosphorus, sulfur, and chlorine. Aluminum chloride, phosphorus pentafluoride, sulfur hexafluoride, and chlorine trifluoride are typical covalent compounds. They must, therefore, contain six, ten, twelve, and ten bonding electrons, respectively.

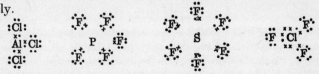

The ions AlF_6^{-3} and SiF_6^{-2} apparently contain twelve bonding electrons.

To be sure, $AlCl_3$ is associated to Al_2Cl_6 at low temperatures, but we shall adopt the custom of not showing association where it does not add to the clarity of the presentation. There is no more reason for habitually indicating the association of $AlCl_3$ than for continually writing dimeric formulas for those carboxylic acids that associate to double molecules. We should not permit irrelevant details to confuse the *chemical* significance of an electronic formula. The formula should correspond as closely as possible with *chemical behavior*. The dimeric formula for $AlCl_3$ obscures the principal feature of its chemistry.

Upon proceeding further in the periodic table, many other examples of covalent compounds containing six, ten, and twelve electrons in the valence shell may be found. Most of these are in groups III, V, and VI of the representative elements (Fig. 2). Several occur in group VII but will be discussed later. The existence of iodine heptafluoride shows that fourteen electrons are possible in the valence shells of some atoms.

Other violations occur also in the related metals (Fig. 2). Tungsten, in addition to the di- and tetrachlorides, forms covalent penta- and hexachlorides, WCl_5 and WCl_6. WBr_5 [1] and WBr_6 are also known. The low boiling point (19.5° C.) of WF_6 indicates that this compound is hexacovalent. In addition to the di-, tri-, and tetrachlorides, molybdenum forms covalent compounds having the formulas $MoCl_5$ and MoF_6. Osmium forms a covalent hexafluoride (b.p. 205° C.) and also an octafluoride, OsF_8, a stable typically covalent compound having a boiling point of 47.3° C. Here is one compound at least having *twice* the number of bonding electrons permitted by the rule of eight.

The examples given above have included only compounds containing simple covalent bonds. Coordination compounds and metal carbonyls offer many more "violations" of the rule of eight. Other examples in which some electrons are not used as bonding electrons (analogous to the lone pair in ammonia) will be discussed subsequently. Turning to a consideration of the valences

---

[1] In view of the rarity of pentacovalency, doubt may arise concerning its existence in WCl_5 and WBr_5. However, the low boiling points of these compounds, together with the fact that the boiling point of the bromide is the higher of the two, may be taken as sufficient evidence for covalency until crystal-structure measurements are made. If the compounds were ionic the reverse order of boiling points would be expected.

of the related metals (Fig. 2) when acting as positive ions, we find that only the positive ions of the elements in the first column conform to the rule of eight. In none of the other twenty-seven elements of the related metals does the loss of electrons leave a completed shell of eight electrons. This fact is obvious in Fig. 2.

Most of the evidence illustrated by the compounds just discussed has been largely neglected in most textbooks. A few such compounds have been considered by them, e.g., phosphorus pentachloride and sulfur hexafluoride, and various devices have been adopted in the attempt to force compliance with the rule of eight. One was the hypothesis of single-electron bonds in such compounds as phosphorus pentachloride and sulfur hexafluoride. It is no doubt true that one-electron bonds do exist in a very few compounds. The hydrogen-molecule ion is evidently held together by one electron, but the bond is much weaker than the electron pair even in this, the most favorable case. If one-electron bonds exist in the boron hydrides, they are still weaker, as shown by the instability of their compounds. To maintain eight valence electrons for the sulfur atom in the hexafluoride would require four one-electron bonds which (because of the large size of the sulfur atom compared to hydrogen or boron) would be far more unstable than those in boron. Yet sulfur hexafluoride is one of the most stable compounds known.[2] In spite of this conclusive evidence, it has been claimed [3] that parachor measurements indicate the presence of one-electron bonds in such compounds. But, as pointed out by R. Samuel, the parachor may lend itself equally well to different schemes of valence, depending upon the original assumptions.[4] Additional exceptions to the rule of eight will be considered in more detail below.

Abandoning the rule of eight would seem to be the first step in acquiring the fuller understanding of valence made possible by the progress in our knowledge of atomic structure.

3. Atomic Orbitals.

According to the quantum theory, the periodic system can be regarded as being built up from hydrogen by adding one proton

[2] Eméleus and Anderson, *Modern Aspects of Inorganic Chemistry*, D. Van Nostrand Company, New York, 1939.

[3] Sugden, *The Parachor and Valency*, F. S. Crofts and Co., New York, 1930

[4] Samuel, *J. Chem. Phys.*, **12**, 180 (1944).

at a time (plus the required number of neutrons) to the nucleus and one electron at a time to the atom outside the nucleus. From the periodic table and spectroscopic data it is deduced that the

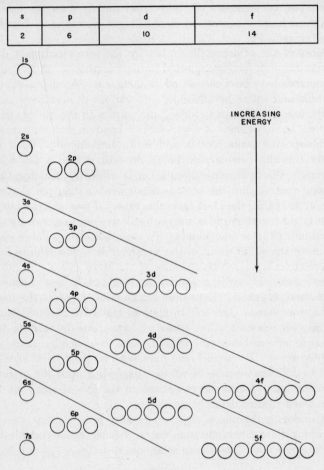

s	p	d	f
2	6	10	14

INCREASING ENERGY

FIG. 1.

electrons arrange themselves in main levels and sublevels in a regular way, as shown in Fig. 1. Figure 1 is a plot of approximate relative energy levels.[5] Each circle represents one atomic orbital. On paper each circle may be regarded as a box that can be occupied

[5] Luder, Vernon, and Zuffanti, *General Chemistry*, W. B. Saunders Company, Philadelphia, 1959.

either by one electron or by two electrons spinning in opposite directions.

The numbers in Fig. 1 are different values of the principal quantum number n. Each main level is designated by one value of the principal quantum number. The letters s, p, d, f correspond to the values 0, 1, 2, 3 for the orbital quantum number l, which determines the "eccentricity" of the orbital. The difference in eccentricity leads to sublevels in the main levels. Both types of numbers must be used in the equations for the energy of the orbitals. The orbital quantum number has a series of values for each value of n:
$$l = 0, 1, 2, 3 \cdots n - 1$$

For example, in the third main level ($n = 3$) there are three sublevels ($l = 0, 1, 2$) designated $3s$, $3p$, $3d$. From spectroscopic data obtained when the atoms are placed in a magnetic field it is found that s sublevels always contain one orbital, p sublevels always contain three orbitals, d sublevels contain five orbitals, and f sublevels contain seven orbitals. It is obvious from Fig. 1 that in the higher energy levels there is considerable overlapping of main levels. Furthermore, some of the closer levels apparently interchange occasionally.

In general, the electrons occupy the lowest energy levels first. One electron goes into each orbital in a given sublevel (one line in Fig. 1) until each of the orbitals in that sublevel is occupied by one electron. When every orbital in a given sublevel contains one electron they begin filling up with two electrons in each orbital. Two electrons in an orbital are said to be coupled or paired. Supposedly, the opposite spins of coupled electrons result in electromagnetic attraction more than sufficient to overcome the repulsion of like charges.

The way in which electrons are added to the orbitals can be made clearer by considering some examples from Fig. 2. From the chart the electron configuration of aluminum is seen to be

$$_{13}\text{Al } 1s^2 \, 2s^2 \, 2p^6 \, 3s^2 \, 3p$$

where the superscripts represent the number of electrons in each *kind* of orbital. If we wish to use the superscripts to represent the number of electrons in *each* orbital, the three $2p$ orbitals must be separated as follows:

$$_{13}\text{Al } 1s^2 \, 2s^2 \, 2p^2 \, 2p^2 \, 2p^2 \, 3s^2 \, 3p$$

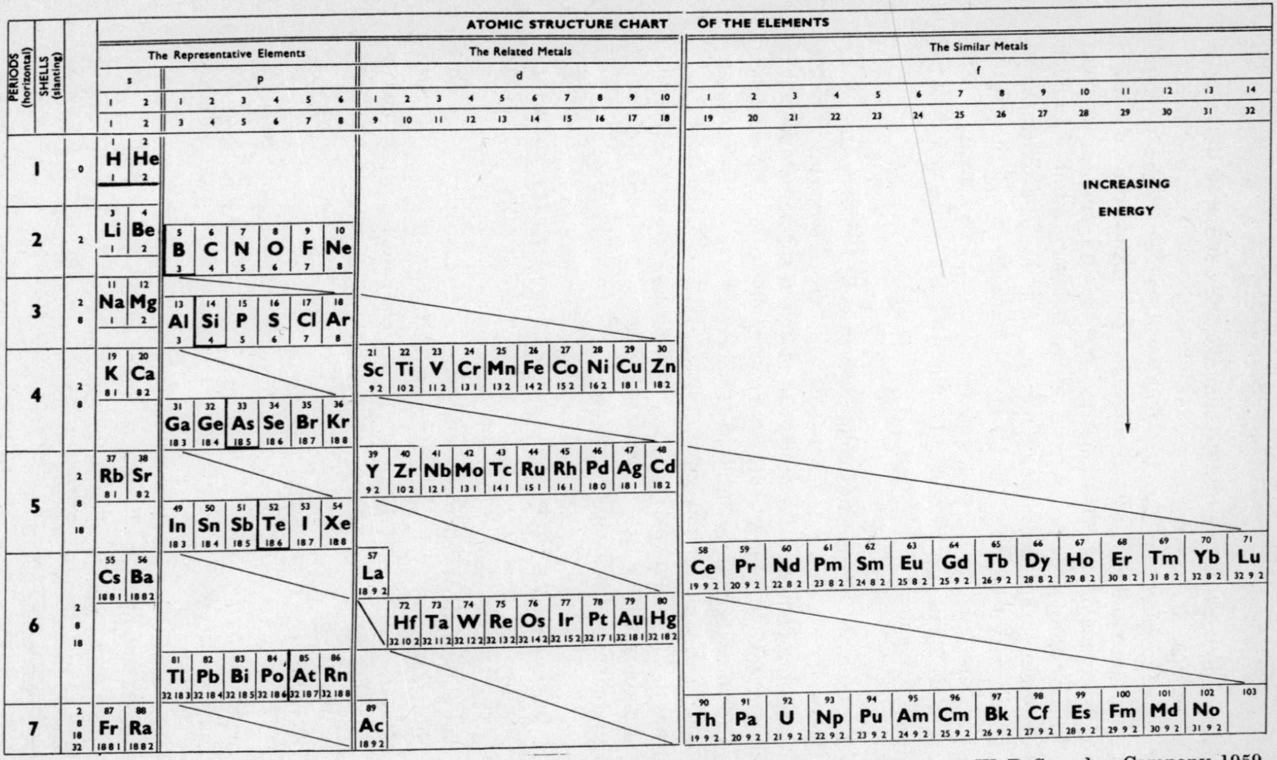

ATOMIC STRUCTURE CHART OF THE ELEMENTS

PERIODS (horizontal)	SHELLS (slanting)	The Representative Elements (s, p)	The Related Metals (d)	The Similar Metals (f)

The Representative Elements — s (1, 2); p (1 2 3 4 5 6)

The Related Metals — d (1 2 3 4 5 6 7 8 9 10)

The Similar Metals — f (1 2 3 4 5 6 7 8 9 10 11 12 13 14)

INCREASING ENERGY →

Period 1: H, He

Period 2: Li Be — B C N O F Ne

Period 3: Na Mg — Al Si P S Cl Ar

Period 4: K Ca — Sc Ti V Cr Mn Fe Co Ni Cu Zn — Ga Ge As Se Br Kr

Period 5: Rb Sr — Y Zr Nb Mo Tc Ru Rh Pd Ag Cd — In Sn Sb Te I Xe

Period 6: Cs Ba — La — Hf Ta W Re Os Ir Pt Au Hg — Tl Pb Bi Po At Rn

Period 7: Fr Ra — Ac

f-block (upper): Ce Pr Nd Pm Sm Eu Gd Tb Dy Ho Er Tm Yb Lu (58–71)

f-block (lower): Th Pa U Np Pu Am Cm Bk Cf Es Fm Md No Lw (90–103)

FIG. 2.

Luder, Vernon, and Zuffanti, *General Chemistry*, W. B. Saunders Company, 1959.

Remembering that the orbitals take electrons one at a time until each orbital in a given sublevel has one electron in it before coupling begins, we take the electron configurations from the chart and write them as follows (writing the $2p$ orbitals together since there is no change in them):

Silicon

$$_{14}Si\ 1s^2\ 2s^2\ 2p^6\ 3s^2\ 3p\ 3p$$

Phosphorus

$$_{15}P\ 1s^2\ 2s^2\ 2p^6\ 3s^2\ 3p\ 3p\ 3p$$

Sulfur

$$_{16}S\ 1s^2\ 2s^2\ 2p^6\ 3s^2\ 3p^2\ 3p\ 3p$$

Chlorine

$$_{17}Cl\ 1s^2\ 2s^2\ 2p^6\ 3s^2\ 3p^2\ 3p^2\ 3p$$

Note that phosphorus has three unpaired p electrons, but that, since there can be only three p orbitals, sulfur has only two unpaired electrons and chlorine only one.

The five atoms just discussed may be written as follows:

$$:Al\cdot \qquad :\overset{\cdot}{Si}\cdot \qquad :\overset{\cdot}{P}\cdot \qquad :\overset{\cdot}{S}: \qquad :\overset{\cdot\cdot}{Cl}:$$

Written in this way, the symbols indicate the paired and unpaired electrons of the valence shell. For example, the symbol for phosphorus now shows the two paired $3s$ electrons and the three unpaired $3p$ electrons.

For those elements which have *two* incomplete shells (main levels), i.e., most of the related metals (Fig. 2),[6] valence bonds to other atoms often involve both shells. The original Lewis conventions provided no way to represent such atoms, but if the rule of eight is abandoned and the convention just proposed is adopted, the method is obvious. Dots representing the electrons in *both* shells should be used, regardless of how many may be required. No distinction between the two energy levels need be made since they are so close together, even closer than indicated in Fig. 1. The vertical lines on the right of Fig. 1 joining the $4s$ with the $3d$, the $5s$ with the $4d$, and the $6s$ and $4f$ with the $5d$ sublevels are used to indicate that there is practically no difference. Actually, these levels may interchange in different atoms.

[6] Luder, *J. Chem. Education*, **20**, 21 (1943). Note added to second edition: For a brief explanation of Fig. 2, see the Preface to Dover Edition, p. vii.

From Fig. 2, we see that manganese has the electron configuration:

$$_{25}Mn\ 1s^2\ 2s^2\ 2p^6\ 3s^2\ 3p^6\ 3d\ 3d\ 3d\ 3d\ 3d\ 4s^2$$

The seven valence electrons are the two paired $4s$ electrons and the five single or unpaired electrons, with practically no difference in energy among the seven. The electronic symbol would be

$$:\overset{..}{Mn}\cdot$$

with two dots close together for the paired $4s$ electrons and the other five far enough apart so as to represent five unpaired electrons. For iron

$$_{26}Fe\ 1s^2\ 2s^2\ 2p^6\ 3s^2\ 3p^6\ 3d^2\ 3d\ 3d\ 3d\ 3d\ 4s^2$$

the electronic symbol would be

$$:\overset{..\ ..}{Fe}\cdot$$

showing eight valence electrons, four paired and four single. For cobalt

$$_{27}Co\ 1s^2\ 2s^2\ 2p^6\ 3s^2\ 3p^6\ 3d^2\ 3d^2\ 3d\ 3d\ 3d\ 4s^2$$

the electronic symbol would be

$$:\overset{..\ ..}{Co}\cdot$$

showing nine valence electrons, six paired and three single. For nickel

$$_{28}Ni\ 1s^2\ 2s^2\ 2p^6\ 3s^2\ 3p^6\ 3d^2\ 3d^2\ 3d^2\ 3d\ 3d\ 4s^2$$

the electronic symbol would be

$$:\overset{..\ ..}{N}\ \overset{..}{i}\cdot$$

showing ten valence electrons, eight paired and two single. At the end of the row with zinc there is again only one level in the valence shell, consisting of the two $4s$ electrons. The $3d$ orbitals are now fully occupied.

The advantages of writing electronic symbols in the manner suggested will become more fully apparent with the discussion of valence.

To summarize: (1) The order in which atoms are built up by the addition of electrons to the corresponding nucleus is: $1s$, $2s$, $2p$, $3s$, $3p$, ($4s$, $3d$), $4p$, ($5s$, $4d$), $5p$, ($6s$, $5d$, $4f$), $6p$, $7s$, $5f$, according to Fig. 1. (The parentheses are used to indicate that these levels have about the same energy and may even change their order in different elements). (2) All the orbitals in a given sublevel must contain one electron apiece before pairing of spins begins to complete the orbitals with two electrons in each. (3) Electronic symbols should be written showing all paired and unpaired electrons in the valence shell. Since in many atoms the valence shell includes electrons from two energy levels, as many as eleven dots (as in Cu) may often be required.

4. The Origin of Valence.

When we turn to a consideration of chemical compounds, a natural assumption to make as a starting point is: *Uncompleted orbitals in one atom may be filled by electrons from another atom.*[7] This filling of orbitals in a given atom may be done by loose electrons (resulting in electrovalence) or by electrons that remain in the other atoms (resulting in covalence).

The italicized statement may be called the rule of two. Both electrovalence and covalence are due to pairing of electrons to fill incomplete orbitals. Because it is only for $n = 2$ that the maximum number of electrons is eight, the rule of eight and the rule of two are approximately equivalent only for the second period. For the third period $n = 3$ which means nine orbitals holding a maximum of eighteen electrons. Considerations of charge and space in addition to an insufficient number of electrons prevent this number from being approached in the third period except by compounds such as phosphorus pentafluoride and sulfur hexafluoride and by ions like AlF_6^{-3} and SiF_6^{-2}. In this period and the later ones, the number of electrons in the valence shells of the atoms in molecules may seem at first glance to be quite unpredictable, but the rule of two in conjunction with a table of electron configurations often will solve the problem. Several examples will now be considered under the separate headings of electrovalence and covalence.

The only rule to be followed is that uncompleted orbitals in one atom may be filled by electrons from another atom. It is called the rule of two because a completed orbital contains two electrons.

[7] Many readers will immediately recognize that the discussion owes its origin primarily to London (*Z. Physik,* **46,** 455 [1928]). However, they will also note certain modifications as the argument proceeds.

5. Electrovalence.

Since substitution of the rule of two for the rule of eight makes little difference as far as the electrovalences of the representative elements (Fig. 2) are concerned, they will not be discussed here. Neither will the rare earths be considered. Readers interested in the rare earths may consult the *Journal of Chemical Education* for an article by Pearce and Selwood.[8]

One fact should be mentioned before we proceed with a brief discussion of the related metals (Fig. 2). Practically no monatomic negative ions have a charge larger than -2. Very few monatomic positive ions have a charge larger than $+3$. For example, some people have been accustomed to think of "stannic ion" as having a valence of $+4$, but actually, there is no such thing as a stannic ion in pure stannic chloride, a typical covalent compound. Even in water the stannic ion has no existence as a monatomic ion with four positive charges on it. Apparently, insufficient energy is involved in ordinary chemical reactions to build up charges larger than -2 or $+3$ on single atoms. According to Coulomb's law, the size of the atoms involved must also have an important bearing upon the formation of ions, so that beryllium, a small atom, does not show much tendency to form a positive ion.

Because the rule of two centers attention on those atoms in a molecule that are completing their orbitals in the combination, it does not add much to a discussion of the related metals as positive ions. However, it might be well to point out that the related metals do not violate the rule of two as they do the rule of eight. As mentioned previously, few of the many positive ions of these metals conform to the rule of eight, but the rule of two does not specify the nature of the positive ion. The number of electrons removable to complete the orbitals of some other atom is determined by size and charge as well as by the numbers of unpaired electrons.

For example, the electronic configuration of iron is

$$_{26}\text{Fe } 1s^2 \; 2s^2 \; 2p^6 \; 3s^2 \; 3p^6 \; 3d^2 \; 3d \; 3d \; 3d \; 3d \; 4s^2$$

and the electronic symbol showing electrons from both incomplete shells as valence electrons is

$$:\overset{\textstyle \cdots}{\underset{\textstyle \cdot \; \cdot}{\text{F}}}\text{e}\cdot$$

[8] Pearce and Selwood, *J. Chem. Education*, **13**, 363 (1936).

It is easy to remove two electrons to give the ferrous ion, a little more difficult to remove a third one, and impossible because of the strong electrical field to remove the fourth electron by ordinary chemical means. Most of the ions of the related metals are left with unpaired electrons, as is shown by their color and paramagnetism.

6. Covalence.

When atoms complete one or more orbitals to form covalent bonds, the number of pairs shared between them depends upon various factors, including: (1) the number of unpaired electrons in each atom, (2) spatial considerations. Bearing the second factor in mind, we shall emphasize the first. We shall do so by first applying the rule of two to each compound chosen as an example as if it were formed from neutral atoms whose electron configurations are given in Fig. 2.

Considering the representative elements first, we find that the maximum number of valence electrons for elements in the second period according to Fig. 1 is eight.[9] Beryllium and boron chlorides have already been discussed sufficiently to illustrate compounds in which the maximum of eight is not reached. The properties of boron trichloride as a strong acid [10] make it apparent that the one empty orbital of the boron atom can still be filled by two paired electrons from an atom in a basic molecule. The remaining four active elements in the second period require no further discussion, since for them the rule of two becomes equivalent to the rule of eight, except, perhaps, in carbon monoxide.

In the third period (only the representative elements in that period being considered for the time being) the number of orbitals is nine. The tendency of magnesium to fill up its orbitals seems to be the reason for the activity of Grignard reagents. The tendency of aluminum chloride to fill up an empty orbital in the aluminum atom results in its familiar activity as an acid catalyst.[11] The formation of SiF_6^{-2} ion apparently involves the filling of two orbitals of silicon in silicon tetrafluoride by paired electrons

[9] R. Samuel (see note 4) mentions the possible existence of nitrogen pentafluoride. Such a compound if it does exist would involve promotion from $n = 2$ to $n = 3$.

[10] Chapter 3.

[11] Chapters 9 and 10.

from two fluoride ions to give a total of twelve electrons.[12] Carbon in the preceding period cannot do this because in its compounds all its orbitals are filled by eight electrons.

The phosphorus atom has two paired and three single electrons in its valence shell, and so phosphorus trifluoride is written (using crosses for phosphorus electrons):

Phosphorus pentafluoride must be formed by uncoupling the lone pair of 3s electrons. This reaction may be formally represented as follows:

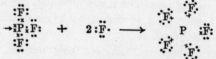

where the small arrow indicates that the two paired electrons are uncoupled during the reaction. Actually, the two fluorine atoms are combined in a molecule and the paired electrons between them must also be uncoupled, but they are written separately for simplicity. This uncoupling of paired electrons requires energy, but not more than the reaction can amply supply, since the compound is formed and is fairly stable. The extreme instability of nitrogen pentafluoride, if it exists at all,[4] must be due to the fact that the nitrogen atom has no more orbitals available for which $n = 2$, and promotion of electrons from $n = 2$ to $n = 3$ would require more energy than its synthesis can furnish.[13]

[12] The question which arises at this point, namely, what determines in detail the number of atoms grouped about the central atom in such cases, is beyond the scope of the discussion in this chapter. Suffice it to say here that completion of orbitals may be opposed by the repulsion of built-up charges or hindered by lack of space for enough atoms to gather around the central atom.

[13] The pentachloride (Powell, Clark, and Wells, *J. Chem. Soc.*, **1942**, 642) and pentabromide (Powell and Clark, *Nature*, **145**, 971 [1940]) of phosphorus have been the subject of crystal structure investigations which have shown them to be ionic in the solid state. The ions are PCl_4^{+1} and PCl_6^{-1} for the chloride and PBr_4^{+1} and Br^{-1} for the bromide. This fact does not mean that they are not covalent in the gaseous state, nor does it imply that PF_5 is not pentacovalent in all three states. The boiling point for the fluoride is far below the boiling points of the chloride and bromide. If the fluoride were ionic, its boiling point would be higher.

The series of sulfur compounds S_2F_2, SF_2, SF_4, S_2F_{10}, SF_6 offers an interesting application of the rule of two. The sulfur atom has two electron pairs and two single electrons:

$$\overset{\times\times}{\underset{\times\times}{\times S \times}}$$

SF_2 must be formed by direct pairing of the two unpaired electrons in the sulfur atom:

$$:\overset{..}{\underset{..}{F}}\overset{..\ \times\times\ ..}{\underset{..\ \times\times\ ..}{\times S \times}}\overset{..}{\underset{..}{F}}:$$

The formation of SF_4 involves the uncoupling of one pair, leading to ten electrons in the sulfur valence shell. Both pairs are uncoupled in SF_6, giving a total of twelve:

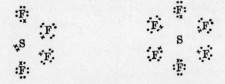

Two different electronic formulas have been suggested for S_2F_2: [14]

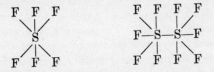

The chemical evidence for a choice between the two seems inconclusive. In the second formula, two of the paired electrons on the upper sulfur atom have been uncoupled to pair off with the two unpaired electrons of the lower sulfur atom. Thus the upper sulfur atom has ten electrons in its valence shell.

S_2F_{10} resembles SF_6 to some extent in its chemical properties but is more reactive.[2] The electronic formula is similar in that in both molecules the sulfur atoms have twelve valence electrons:

F F F   F F   F F
\ | /   \ | | /
  S   F—S—S—F
/ | \   / | | \
F F F   F F   F F

The interhalogen compounds of the types AB_3, AB_5, and AB_7 are also interesting examples of the rule of two. ICl_3 must involve

[14] Samuel, *J. Chem. Phys.*, **12**, 380 (1944).

the uncoupling of two of the paired electrons in the iodine atom of iodine monochloride:

In this formula there are ten electrons in the valence shell of iodine. In iodine pentachloride there must be twelve, one more pair being uncoupled:

Iodine heptafluoride should be written with fourteen valence electrons, all seven of the original iodine electrons being shared with the seven fluorine atoms:

$$
\begin{array}{ccc}
F & F & F \\
 & \diagdown \,|\, \diagup & \\
F & -\,I\,- & F \\
 & \diagup \quad \diagdown & \\
F & & F
\end{array}
$$

From these examples, chosen from the representative elements, it is apparent that the rule of two more often than the rule of eight gives the correct result when molecules are considered as if formed in the same way as the periodic system is built up. A few more examples taken from the related metals will be considered next.

The older eight-column periodic charts obscured the similarities observed in the chemical properties of the related metals. The type of chart illustrated by Fig. 2 clears up this source of confusion. Atoms of related metals have either one or two electrons in the outermost shell and therefore behave primarily as metals. Most of them have two electrons in the last shell, and from the chemist's point of view most of the remainder could be considered as having two also. Their similarities when acting as cations have already been considered.

In spite of their primary characteristics as metals, some of them in *one* respect do behave as non-metals. Chromium and manganese, for example, form with oxygen negative ions that correspond to sulfate and perchlorate ions. Yet neither chromium nor manganese form negative "chromide" or "manganide" ions, comparable to sulfide and chloride ions. The answer to this apparent contradiction lies in the fact that most of the related metals have two incomplete shells of practically the same energy. Therefore, all the electrons in both shells should be considered valence electrons in writing electronic formulas.

As an example, let us compare the behavior of sulfur and chromium. Sulfur and oxygen atoms both have six valence electrons, two electron pairs and two single electrons in each:

Applying the rule of two, we may imagine sulfuric acid as being formed in the following way: First, the two incomplete orbitals in each oxygen can be filled with two electrons from one sulfur atom and two electrons from two hydrogen atoms:

$$H:\overset{..}{\underset{..}{O}}:\overset{xx}{\underset{xx}{S}}:\overset{..}{\underset{..}{O}}:H \quad \text{(hypothetical)}$$

Two more oxygen atoms, each with two unpaired electrons, can then complete their orbitals by uncoupling the two electron pairs on the sulfur atom and forming double bonds:

$$\overset{..}{\underset{..}{O}}$$
$$H:\overset{..}{\underset{..}{O}}:\overset{xx}{\underset{xx}{S}}:\overset{..}{\underset{..}{O}}:H$$
$$\overset{..}{\underset{..}{O}}:$$

Note that there are twelve electrons in the valence shell of the sulfur atom according to the rule of two. The customary way of writing the formula with only eight electrons was adopted primarily to force compliance with the rule of eight.[15]

The chromate is formed in a similar way. Representing the five unpaired $3d$ electrons and the one $4s$ electron as being in the same valence shell, we find that chromium has the same number of valence electrons as sulfur:

$$\overset{x\ x}{\underset{x\ x}{\times Cr \times}}$$

The one electron on the left may be considered the $4s$ electron, but this distinction is not important, since all are practically

[15] This return to "classical" formulas will be considered further in section 7.

equivalent (Fig. 1).   The first step in the formation of chromic acid can be represented in the same way as with sulfuric acid:

$$H:\overset{\cdot\cdot}{\underset{\cdot\cdot}{O}}\overset{xx}{\underset{xx}{\times}}\overset{\cdot\cdot}{\underset{\cdot\cdot}{O}}:H \quad \text{(hypothetical)}$$

The next step is different only in that the four remaining electrons are already single; hence no uncoupling by the oxygen atoms is necessary:

The reason that the Cr^{-2} ion does not exist is that such an ion would still contain four unpaired electrons and would be too unstable.   To fill all six incomplete orbitals to form a monatomic ion would give it a charge of -6, which is much too great a charge to build up against the Coulomb repulsion.

Similar analysis indicates that fourteen electrons are shared in perchloric and permanganic acids:

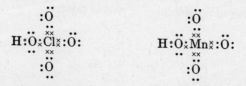

All four of these formulas are equivalent to the *old formulas used before electrons were discovered*, e.g.,

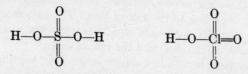

showing a valence of two for oxygen, six for sulfur, and seven for chlorine.   Anticipating objections to the idea of fourteen electrons for chlorine, we may recall the interhalogen compounds AB_5 and AB_7.   In these compounds, the relative sizes of the two atoms seem to determine whether the compounds will be formed.   So far, there is no known chlorine pentafluoride, but BrF_5 and IF_7 do exist.   Apparently there is not room enough for five fluorine atoms around one chlorine atom.   But there are only four oxygen

atoms involved in perchloric acid. If fourteen electrons are holding seven other atoms to iodine in the heptafluoride, it does not
seem unreasonable to find that fourteen electrons are holding
four oxygen atoms to chlorine.

The series of osmium halides $OsCl_3$, $OsCl_4$, OsF_6, OsF_8 is interesting. The electronic symbol for the osmium atom is similar to
that of iron, with two $6s$ electrons and two $5d$ electrons paired,
leaving four $5d$ electrons unpaired:

$OsCl_3$ is ionic, affording one example of the relatively small number of trivalent ions. Three of the four electrons can be removed,
but not a fourth, since $OsCl_4$ is not ionic but covalent

with a total of twelve electrons for the osmium valence shell. The
osmium atom in OsF_6 must have fourteen electrons in its
valence shell,

and the osmium atom in OsF_8 must have sixteen electrons:

F   F   F
 \ | /
F—Os—F
 / | \
F   F   F

The failure of the related metal carbonyls and nitrosyls to obey
the rule of eight was recognized very early. So it is not surprising
that our present concepts of their valence relationships already
are so close to the ideas presented here that no further discussion
of them is necessary.

Discussion of other covalent compounds of the related metals
would be interesting, but in regard to most of them it would be
merely speculation, since insufficient experimental data are available. However, the above examples of covalent compounds,

together with those considered in the previous section, should be sufficient to illustrate the application of the rule of two to the problem of valence. It is evident that proper use of the rule of two demands both application of our knowledge of atomic orbitals and modification of our present method of writing electronic symbols so as to represent two partly filled energy levels of practically the same energy as one valence shell.

7. Electron Affinity.

Though substituting the rule of two for the rule of eight effects some improvement in the theory of valence, it is still far from being a completely satisfactory theory. So far in our discussion reference to any tendency opposing the filling of atomic orbitals has been omitted deliberately. That there is such a tendency becomes obvious upon considering the following example. The formation of sulfur monoxide might be represented as due to the sharing of the two unpaired electrons in each atom:

$$\overset{xx}{\underset{xx}{\times S \times}} + \cdot \overset{..}{O} \cdot \rightarrow \overset{xx}{\underset{xx}{S \times}} \overset{..}{:} \overset{..}{O}$$

But the attraction of the oxygen atom for electrons is stronger than that of the sulfur atom. Chemists are familiar with the qualitative manifestation of this fact in the representative elements (Fig. 2). A more exact comparison is given in Table 1. (The larger numbers represent more attraction for electrons.)

TABLE 1

FIRST IONIZATION POTENTIALS (IN VOLTS)

(Data from Sisler and Vanderwerf, *J. Chem. Education*, **22**, 390 [1945].)

H	He					
13.53	24.48					
Li	Be	B	C	N	O	F
5.37	9.28	8.33	11.22	14.48	13.55	18.6
Na	Mg	Al	Si	P	S	Cl
5.12	7.61	5.96	8.12	11.1	10.31	12.96

How to take account of this difference in attraction for electrons is a difficult and still unsettled problem. For a single bond, the difference might be represented by writing the electrons closer to the more electrophilic (electron-attracting) atom. But for a double bond, such as we have tentatively written for sulfur monoxide, it might better be pictured as follows:

$$:\overset{\cdot\cdot}{\text{S}}::\overset{\cdot\cdot}{\text{O}}: \leftrightarrow :\overset{\cdot\cdot}{\text{S}}:\overset{\cdot\cdot}{\underset{\cdot\cdot}{\text{O}}}:$$

This formula corresponds, perhaps, a little better to the instability of sulfur monoxide. But probably neither the double-bond (as first written) nor the single-bond formula represents the actual molecule. This state of affairs apparently holds for many other molecules. It has led to the theories of resonance and of molecular orbitals. For reasons discussed below, neither of these theories will be extensively used in this book. At any rate, the condition of "strain" in molecules like sulfur monoxide, as the formula is written on the basis of our knowledge of atomic orbitals, cannot be ignored. A redistribution of electrons among all orbitals to give the most stable arrangement in view of the two opposing tendencies must be contemplated. A possible way out of the dilemma is to write formulas generally according to the rule of two but modified where necessary to show as far as possible the potentialities of the compounds for chemical reaction. (This would mean usually ignoring association between identical molecules.)

To illustrate this principle the following formulas may be considered:

$$\begin{array}{ccccc}
 & & :\overset{\cdot\cdot}{\text{O}}: & \left[\begin{array}{c} :\overset{\cdot\cdot}{\text{O}}: \\ :\overset{\cdot\cdot}{\text{O}}:\overset{\cdot\cdot}{\text{S}}:\overset{\cdot\cdot}{\text{O}}: \\ :\overset{\cdot\cdot}{\underset{\cdot\cdot}{\text{O}}}: \end{array}\right]^{-2} & :\overset{\cdot\cdot}{\text{O}} \\
:\overset{\cdot\cdot}{\text{S}}:\overset{\cdot\cdot}{\underset{\cdot\cdot}{\text{O}}}: & :\overset{\cdot\cdot}{\text{O}}:\overset{\cdot\cdot}{\text{S}}:\overset{\cdot\cdot}{\underset{\cdot\cdot}{\text{O}}}: & :\overset{\cdot\cdot}{\text{O}}:\overset{\cdot\cdot}{\underset{\cdot\cdot}{\text{S}}}:\overset{\cdot\cdot}{\underset{\cdot\cdot}{\text{O}}}: & & \text{H}:\overset{\cdot\cdot}{\text{O}}:\overset{\cdot\cdot}{\underset{\cdot\cdot}{\text{S}}}:\overset{\cdot\cdot}{\underset{\cdot\cdot}{\text{O}}}:\text{H} \\
 & & & & :\overset{\cdot\cdot}{\underset{\cdot\cdot}{\text{O}}} \\
\text{I} & \text{II} & \text{III} & \text{IV} & \text{V}
\end{array}$$

Note that the first three formulas show six electrons, the fourth eight, and the fifth twelve for the sulfur atom. The number increases from eight to twelve (from formulas IV to V) because of the electron affinity of the protons. Consider that the two protons added to a sulfate ion cause the redistribution of electrons. We imagine the positive protons shifting all electrons toward themselves. This makes the sulfur atom more positive, as shown below:

$$\text{H}\overset{\cdot\cdot}{\underset{}{\leftarrow}}\overset{:\overset{\cdot\cdot}{\text{O}}:)}{\underset{:\overset{\cdot\cdot}{\text{O}}:)}{\text{O}\leftrightarrow\text{S}\rightarrow\text{O}}}\overset{}{\rightarrow}\text{H} \longleftrightarrow \text{H}:\overset{:\overset{\cdot\cdot}{\text{O}}:}{\underset{:\overset{\cdot\cdot}{\text{O}}:}{\overset{\cdot\cdot}{\text{O}}:\text{S}:\overset{\cdot\cdot}{\text{O}}:}}\text{H}$$

Thus the number of electrons on the sulfur atom is increased to twelve. This return to the "classical" structures for such oxy-acids as

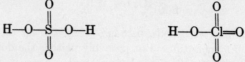

with twelve and fourteen electrons, is supported by Phillips, Hunter, and Sutton.[16] They also suggest that the stability of such acids is actually due to the formation of the double bonds. This accounts for the fact that fluorine does not form such acids.[16] Since fluorine has only four orbitals, no double bonds can be formed.

If we regard each electronic formula as dynamic rather than static, there is little to be gained by emphasizing the concept of resonance hybrids. Furthermore, the detailed theory of resonance has come under heavy fire.[17] It is claimed by A. Burawoy[17] that ". . . the interpretation of polyatomic structures does not require the hypothesis of resonance among several idealized valence-bond structures, a speculative application of the quantum-mechanical conception of resonance, which is in disagreement with numerous facts." In view of this controversy, we shall avoid *detailed* application of the theory of resonance. The theory of molecular orbitals, an alternative treatment, is too complex for the present discussion.

It is important to bear in mind the dynamic nature of electronic formulas, which arises from the two opposing tendencies which must be balanced in the electron distribution of many molecules. We shall encounter more examples in later chapters, but we mention only two additional examples here, carbon dioxide and aldehydes:

$$:\ddot{O}::C::\ddot{O}: \qquad \begin{matrix} H\ H \\ H:\ddot{C}:\ddot{C}::\ddot{O}: \\ \ddot{H} \end{matrix}$$

8. The Coordinate Covalent Bond.

Another way in which orbitals in one atom may be filled by electrons from another atom is exemplified by the molecule of

[16] Phillips, Hunter, and Sutton, *J. Chem. Soc.*, **1945**, 146.

[17] Burawoy, *Nature*, **155**, 328 (1945); Burawoy, *Chemistry & Industry*, **51**, 434 (1944).

the covalent compound boron trichloride. The maximum number of orbitals available for compound formation in atoms of the second period is four, one $2s$ and three $2p$ orbitals. In boron trichloride, only three are filled:

$$\ddot{:}\overset{\cdot\cdot}{Cl}:$$
$$\overset{\cdot\cdot}{:Cl}\overset{\cdot\cdot}{:}\overset{\cdot\cdot}{B}$$
$$\overset{\cdot\cdot}{:Cl}:$$
$$\overset{}{\cdot\cdot}$$

The fourth may be filled by a lone pair of electrons from another molecule, e.g., ammonia, to form an addition compound:

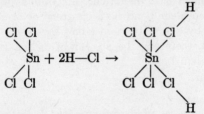

$$\begin{array}{ccc} Cl & H \\ | & | \\ Cl-B & + \quad :N-H \quad \rightarrow \\ | & | \\ Cl & H \end{array} \qquad \begin{array}{cc} Cl & H \\ | & | \\ Cl-B:N-H \\ | & | \\ Cl & H \end{array}$$

In the past, this reaction has been regarded as another confirmation of the rule of eight. Actually the limitation of eight electrons exists only for the second period, as we have already pointed out. In the third period, five more orbitals are available, more in the later periods. In a large number of compounds, some of the additional orbitals are used for coordinate covalent bond formation.

The electrical "strain" involved in the formation of a coordinate covalent bond may result in subsequent ionization to form such ions as

$$AlF_6^{-3} \qquad SnCl_6^{-2} \qquad ZrF_7^{-3} \qquad Mo(CN)_8^{-4}$$

all of which fail to obey the rule of eight. The reaction between stannic chloride and hydrogen chloride may be represented formally as follows:

$$\begin{array}{ccc} Cl \ \ Cl \\ \backslash \ | \\ Sn + 2H-Cl \rightarrow \\ / \ | \\ Cl \ \ Cl \end{array} \qquad \begin{array}{ccc} & & H \\ & & / \\ Cl \ Cl \ Cl \\ \backslash \ | \ / \\ Sn \\ / \ | \ \backslash \\ Cl \ Cl \ Cl \\ & & \backslash \\ & & H \end{array}$$

Subsequent ionization may depend upon the environment; nevertheless, the tin atom is using six of its orbitals (containing twelve electrons in all) for bonding purposes.

At one time, the hydrogen bridge was regarded by some chemists as an example of coordination. Chelation and association, such as often occur between carboxyl groups, were thought to indicate the existence of 2-covalent hydrogen. The formulas were written to show the hydrogen bonded by two electron pairs, e.g., in the following formula to show the dimeric association of acetic acid:

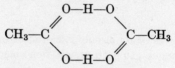

Two-covalent hydrogen is now regarded as unlikely, in view of the large energy difference between $1s$ and $2s$ orbitals (as shown in Fig. 1). Two electrons are the maximum for the hydrogen atom. The forces holding the hydrogen atoms to the carbonyl oxygens are probably electrostatic and should be represented by dotted lines:

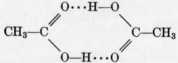

The original definition [18] of the coordinate covalent bond apparently was not intended to imply any fundamental difference between it and any other covalent bond. The word "coordinate" was used merely to indicate an imaginary difference in the way the covalent bond is formed.

In view of the controversies evident [19] in the literature, it seems best to retain the original definition. A coordinate covalent bond is merely any covalent bond both electrons of which were originally supplied by one of the two atoms involved. Once such a bond is formed, there may be no way of distinguishing it from any other covalent bond.

[18] Lewis, *Valence and the Structure of Atoms and Molecules*, The Chemical Catalog Company, New York, 1923; Sidgwick, *The Electronic Theory of Valency*, Oxford University Press, New York, 1927.

[19] (a) Samuel, *J. Chem. Phys.*, **12**, 167, 180, 380 (1944); (b) Wheland, *ibid.*, **13**, 239 (1945); (c) Burawoy, *Trans. Faraday Soc.*, **275**, 537 (1944).

Three examples should be sufficient to illustrate this inability to tell the difference between a covalent bond and a coordinate covalent bond after they have been formed, as we imagine their formation. When we write the (imaginary) equation

$$
\begin{array}{c} H \\ H{:}\ddot{N}{:} \\ \ddot{H} \end{array} + H^{+1} \rightarrow \left[\begin{array}{c} H \\ H{:}\ddot{N}{:}H \\ \ddot{H} \end{array} \right]^{+1}
$$

we see in the ammonia molecule a potential coordinate bond. The nitrogen atom is going to supply both electrons to form a covalent bond. For our convenience, we call this bond a coordinate covalent bond. But upon considering the ammonium ion, we find that we are unable to distinguish this bond from the other bonds, which previously have been called simple covalent bonds (because each atom supplied one electron to the bond). This example is a familiar one, but, in view of the tendency of some authors to write coordinate covalent bonds with charges on each atom, it deserves stronger emphasis.

The second example is more striking. When we write the formula for water as

$$
H{:}\ddot{O}{:}H
$$

it rarely occurs to anyone to consider that the two H—O bonds are anything but covalent. Yet, if we write the abbreviated equation for neutralization in water,

$$
H^{+1} + {:}\ddot{O}{:}H^{-1} \rightarrow H{:}\ddot{O}{:}H
$$

we see that one of the bonds is a coordinate covalent bond. Actually, either bond or both could be regarded as either covalent or coordinate. Since our choice depends only upon the immediately previous history of the molecule, it is obvious that there can be no real distinction between the two types of bonds. This is very well expressed in Gilman [20] by the following graphic illustration:

$$
H \underset{\text{pairing}}{\overset{\text{electron}}{\longrightarrow}} H{-}Cl \overset{\text{coordination}}{\longleftarrow} H^{+1} \longleftarrow {:}Cl{:}^{-1}
$$

Of course many compounds do exist in which the *location* of a coordinate covalent bond can be established. But in these also

[20] Gilman, *Organic Chemistry*, John Wiley & Sons, New York, 1938, p. 1602.

we find that there is no inherent difference in the two types of
bonds except in the way they are formed. In the compound

the coordinate covalent bond is located between the boron and
nitrogen. But it is no different from the other covalent bonds. À
large amount of experimental evidence [16,19] supports this view.
In summarizing some of it, obtained from dipole-moment measurements, Phillips, Hunter, and Sutton [16] conclude, "True coordinate
links appear, therefore, to be nearly of the same length to be expected for a normal, single covalency between the same two
elements." Furthermore, it is well known that, although coordinate covalent bonds are often highly polar, many ordinary
covalent bonds are also highly polar.[19]

In view of this brief summary of the present situation, there
seems to be no justification for the designation of coordinate
covalent bonds by means of plus and minus signs. There is no
difference warranting such a distinction between "normal" and
"coordinate" covalent bonds. The only difference is as stated in
the original definition. A coordinate covalent bond is merely a
covalent bond in which both electrons are thought of as being
supplied by the same atom.

The chemistry of the coordinate covalent bond is largely the
chemistry of acids and bases, the subject of this book.

Chapter 3

THE ELECTRONIC THEORY OF ACIDS AND BASES

1. The Theoretical Interpretation.

The experimental criteria of acid-base phenomena as listed in Chapter 1 are: (1) neutralization, (2) titration with indicators, (3) displacement, and (4) catalysis. When the chemical reactions between substances thus classified as acids or bases are examined in detail, the theoretical explanation of their fundamental nature becomes apparent. *A primary acid is capable of accepting a share in a lone electron pair from a base to form a coordinate covalent bond. A primary base donates a share in a lone electron pair to the acid.* The formation of the coordinate bond is the first step in neutralization reactions:

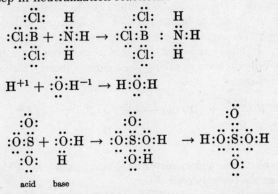

acid   base

Sometimes the product is a covalent compound. At other times, formation of the coordinate bond may be followed—or accompanied—by ionization, so that the product is a salt. For example, the compound $C_5H_5N:AlBr_3$ seems to be a typical salt. Both aluminum bromide and pyridine are covalent compounds. When

43

they are mixed, the white precipitate appears to have the characteristics (e.g., relatively high melting point) of a salt. The electrical "strain" produced by the formation of the coordinate bond may result in the ionization of one of the bromine atoms:

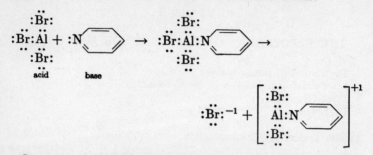

Sometimes formation of the coordinate bond and ionization may be regarded as simultaneous. When the hydrogen bridge was regarded as involving 2-covalent hydrogen, the reaction between hydrogen chloride and water might have been written in similar fashion:

$$H\!:\!\ddot{O}\!: + H\!:\!\ddot{C}l\!: \rightarrow H\!:\!\ddot{O}\!:\!H\!:\!\ddot{C}l\!: \rightarrow H\!:\!\ddot{O}\!:\!H^{+1} + :\!\ddot{C}l\!:^{-1}$$
$$\overset{\displaystyle H}{} \qquad\qquad \overset{\displaystyle H}{} \qquad\qquad \overset{\displaystyle H}{}$$

base   acid

The existence of the hypothetical intermediate addition compound in which the hydrogen bridge between the hydrogen chloride and water molecules involves 2-covalent hydrogen is now regarded as unlikely. Probably it would be better to represent the formation of the coordinate bond as taking place simultaneously with ionization, as follows:

$$H\!:\!\ddot{O}\!: + H\!:\!\ddot{C}l\!: \longrightarrow H\!:\!\ddot{O}\!:\!H^{+1} + :\!\ddot{C}l\!:^{-1}$$
$$\overset{\displaystyle H}{} \qquad\qquad\qquad \overset{\displaystyle H}{}$$

base   acid

Thus the electronic theory pictures the reaction in exactly the same manner as the proton-donor theory.

This example is only one of many which could be given to show that the electronic theory of acids and bases includes the proton theory as a special case. The simultaneous coordination and ionization pictured by the electronic theory is equivalent to the proton-transfer mechanism of the Brønsted theory. The bases of the

Brønsted theory accept protons because they have lone electron pairs that can be used in coordinate-bond formation. All these bases can, therefore, combine with other acceptor molecules in the same way as they do with the proton:

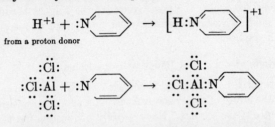

from a proton donor

When we find that aluminum chloride and the proton behave in the same manner in titrations, displacement, and catalysis, as well as in these examples of neutralization, it is clear that we can no longer restrict the name acid to proton donors. To designate acids which owe their acidity to the proton, Lewis [1] suggested the term hydrogen acid (or H-acid).

The electronic theory of acids also includes the theory of solvent systems as a special case. The following reactions are only two of many which could be listed to illustrate this statement.

1. Aluminum chloride and phosgene:

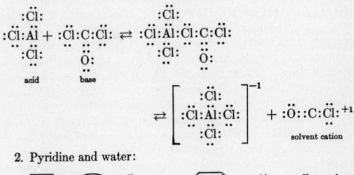

2. Pyridine and water:

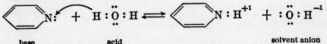

base   acid   solvent anion

The addition of the acid in reaction 1 increases the concentration of solvent cations. The addition of the base in reaction 2 increases

[1] Lewis, *J. Franklin Inst.*, **226**, 293 (1938).

the concentration of solvent anions. The electronic theory gives a fundamental reason for this increased concentration of the ions of the solvent. Acids coordinate with the negative ion of the solvent because the negative ion has lone electron pairs to offer the acid. Bases coordinate with the positive ion of the solvent because the positive ion has a vacant orbital which can accept a lone electron pair from the base.

2. Reactions of Acids and Bases with the Solvent.

The properties of acids and bases with which we are most familiar from the study of water solutions depend to a great extent upon the presence of the solvent. For example, magnesium reacts slowly with hot water, liberating hydrogen. The reaction is much more rapid in acid solution. The difference must be due to the increased concentration of the solvent cation, the hydrogen ion. At first glance, Lewis's theory seems to have little relation to this large body of experimental behavior with which we are so familiar.

For example, Walden [2] has presented the following objections based upon this apparent lack of relationship: (1) the significance of dissociation constants and conductivity measurements would be destroyed; (2) the part played by the solvent would be eliminated; (3) the oppositeness of acids and bases toward indicators would appear to be "purely incidental observations." We have already seen that the oppositeness of acids and bases toward indicators is by no means a purely incidental observation, and we proceed to show that the other two objections are as groundless.

Water may be regarded as the product of the neutralization of hydrogen ion by hydroxide ion. The proton is an acid because it tends to accept an electron pair from a base to fill its $1s$ orbital. The hydroxide ion is a base because the oxygen atom can donate an electron pair to an acid. The formation of the coordinate bond between the proton and the hydroxide ion is neutralization. The question whether the product is actually neutral, in the sense that the donor and acceptor properties of the oxygen and hydrogen atoms are balanced, is probably not of great importance. (Sidgwick[3] believes that the oxygen is "more powerful" as a donor than the hydrogen is as an acceptor).

[2] Walden, *Salts, Acids, and Bases*, McGraw-Hill Book Company, New York, 1929.

[3] Sidgwick, *The Electronic Theory of Valency*, Oxford University Press, New York, 1927.

What is more important is that the relative acidity of water can be compared with that of other solvents. For example, glacial acetic acid is more acidic and liquid ammonia more basic than water. In terms of the electronic theory, this means that acetic acid has a greater tendency to accept an electron pair than water has and that ammonia has a greater tendency to donate an electron pair.

When an acid is dissolved in a solvent, the initial reaction between the acid and the solvent depends primarily upon two factors: the strength of the acid (its tendency to accept an electron pair), and the basic strength of the solvent (its tendency to donate an electron pair). In a given solvent, the strength of the acid can be measured, within the limits of the "leveling effect" of Hantzsch (to be discussed later), by means of the equilibrium constant of the reaction with the solvent. For example, if glacial acetic acid, a typical covalent liquid which conducts an electric current poorly, reacts with water according to the equation

$$HC_2H_3O_2 + H_2O \rightleftarrows H_3O^{+1} + C_2H_3O_2^{-1}$$

the equilibrium constant,

$$K = \frac{[H_3O^{+1}] \times [C_2H_3O_2^{-1}]}{[HC_2H_3O_2]}$$

serves as a measure of acid strength when compared with similar constants for other acids. This is true only if the acid is not too strong. For strong acids like hydrogen chloride, also a typical covalent compound, the reaction proceeds completely to the right in a solvent as basic as water.

Similar conclusions apply to acids that do not contain protons. If the reaction occurring when carbon dioxide, a weak acid, is dissolved in water is represented by the equation (the mechanism will be discussed below)

$$CO_2 + 2H_2O \rightleftarrows H_3O^{+1} + HCO_3^{-1}$$

the equilibrium constant,

$$K = \frac{[H_3O^{+1}] \times [HCO_3^{-1}]}{[CO_2]}$$

may serve as a measure of the acid strength of the carbon dioxide. Strong acids like sulfur trioxide act in the same manner as hydrogen chloride. Sulfur trioxide accepts an electron pair from the oxygen atom in the water molecule just as does the hydrogen in hydrogen chloride. The reaction

$$SO_3 + 2H_2O \rightarrow H_3O^{+1} + HSO_4^{-1}$$

proceeds extensively toward the right. The same considerations hold for such acids as boron chloride, aluminum chloride, or stannic chloride. The boron and aluminum atoms tend to accept an electron pair to complete their s and p orbitals. The tin atom tends to gain two electron pairs as in H_2SnCl_6 to complete two of its d orbitals. There is no valid reason for calling the same type of reaction by two different terms: namely, ionization in the reactions of hydrochloric acid and acetic acid, and hydrolysis in the reactions of sulfur trioxide, carbon dioxide, and stannic chloride. The net result in both types of reaction is an increase in the concentration of the solvent cations. We shall see that this increased concentration of the solvent cations is responsible for most of the familiar properties of acids and bases in water and similar solvents. It is due to the tendency of an acid to accept an electron pair from a base in order to complete the characteristic stable electron configuration of the acid.

The actual mechanism may be regarded in either of two ways, as represented by simplified equations for the reaction between sulfur trioxide and water

$$\overset{\cdot\cdot}{\underset{\cdot\cdot}{:}}\overset{:\overset{\cdot\cdot}{O}:}{\underset{:\overset{\cdot\cdot}{O}:}{O}}\,\overset{\cdot\cdot}{S} + :\overset{\cdot\cdot}{O}:H^{-1},\, H^{+1} \rightarrow \left[:\overset{\cdot\cdot}{\underset{:\overset{\cdot\cdot}{O}:}{O}}:\overset{:\overset{\cdot\cdot}{O}:}{S}:\overset{\cdot\cdot}{O}:H \right]^{-1} + H^{+1}$$

a direct reaction between the sulfur trioxide molecule and the hydroxyl ion; or

$$:\overset{\cdot\cdot}{\underset{:\overset{\cdot\cdot}{O}:}{O}}:\overset{\cdot\cdot}{S} + :\overset{\cdot\cdot}{\underset{H}{O}}:H \rightarrow :\overset{\cdot\cdot}{\underset{:\overset{\cdot\cdot}{O}:H}{O}}:\overset{:\overset{\cdot\cdot}{O}:}{S}:\overset{\cdot\cdot}{O}:H \rightarrow \left[:\overset{\cdot\cdot}{\underset{:\overset{\cdot\cdot}{O}:}{O}}:\overset{:\overset{\cdot\cdot}{O}:}{S}:\overset{\cdot\cdot}{O}:H \right]^{-1} + H^{+1}$$

a direct reaction between the sulfur trioxide molecule and the water molecule, followed by ionization. Either way the result is the same. If the acid is strong enough and if the solvent is basic enough, the concentration of the cation characteristic of the solvent is increased.

In order to show the reaction between carbon dioxide and water, it is necessary to write the formula of the carbon dioxide molecule in its "activated" form (discussed later in connection with secondary acids):

$$\ddot{C} + \ddot{\text{:O:H}} \rightarrow \ddot{C}\ddot{\text{:O:H}} \rightarrow \left[\ddot{C}\ddot{\text{:O:H}} \right]^{-1} + H^{+1}$$

acid   base

Apparently the small number of ions formed is due to the small proportion of activated carbon dioxide molecules. Nevertheless, the concentration of solvent cations is increased in this case also.

The corresponding conclusion holds for bases dissolved in ionizable solvents. The solution contains a higher concentration of anions than the pure solvent. The strength of the base in a given solvent can be estimated from the equilibrium constant. For example, when pyridine is dissolved in water, the pyridine molecule acts as a base in donating an electron pair to the water molecule:

$$C_5H_5N: + HOH \rightleftarrows C_5H_5N:H^{+1} + OH^{-1}$$
base   acid

The equilibrium constant,

$$K = \frac{[C_5H_5N:H^{+1}] \times [OH^{-1}]}{[C_5H_5N]}$$

serves to measure the basic strength of the pyridine.

These examples, purposely chosen with water as the solvent, are enough to show that the part played by the solvent is not "deliberately eliminated." Dissociation constants and conductivity measurements still have as much significance as ever. Walden's objections obviously do not apply. When a sufficiently strong acid reacts with water, the concentration of the hydrogen ion is increased; when a sufficiently strong base reacts with water, the concentration of the hydroxide ion is increased. In a given solvent the strength of an acid or a base, within limits, can be measured by its dissociation constant. There are also many examples in the literature to support this conclusion for solvents other than water.

The typically acid properties of aluminum chloride in phosgene are due to this increased concentration of solvent cations. Germann [4] found that the conductivity of the aluminum chloride solution was less than that of the solution of $Ca(AlCl_4)_2$, and concluded that the acid is rather weak in phosgene. Aluminum chloride is an acid because it accepts an electron pair to fill the vacant p orbital of the aluminum atom. Phosgene is amphoteric and in this reaction is a base. No doubt the resulting cation will be solvated because of the strong tendency of the carbon atom to fill its valence shell. But showing this solvation adds nothing to the discussion, so we may write the equation as

$$AlCl_3 + COCl_2 \rightarrow AlCl_4{}^{-1} + COCl^{+1}$$

The equilibrium constant,

$$K = \frac{[COCl^{+1}] \times [AlCl_4{}^{-1}]}{[AlCl_3]}$$

will serve as a measure of acid strength when compared with the dissociation constants of other acids in phosgene. According to Germann's conductivity measurements K is small, so aluminum chloride is a fairly weak acid in phosgene as a solvent. Similar treatment can be given the results of other investigators.

Meerwein [5] has shown that aluminum alkoxides, when dissolved in alcohols, increase the concentration of the solvent cation in the same manner as aluminum chloride does in phosgene:

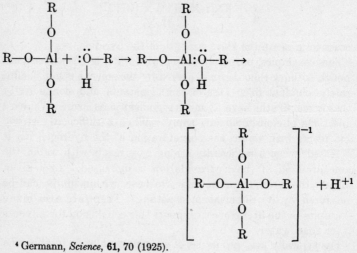

[4] Germann, *Science*, **61**, 70 (1925).
[5] Meerwein, *Ann.* **455**, 227 (1927).

The concentration of the hydrogen ion in the solvent is increased. Other acids, such as boron trifluoride, also increase the hydrogen-ion concentration in organic acids. The work of Jander with sulfur dioxide,[6] that of Smith and others with selenium oxychloride,[7] and some of the work in liquid ammonia can be interpreted in a similar way, not only for acids but for bases as well.

The reason for the solvent-system definitions of Cady and Elsey (Chapter 1) is clear. Acids often do increase the concentration of solvent cations; bases often increase the concentration of solvent anions. However, this does not always happen. When acids react with solvents like ether and pyridine, ionization to give a cation characteristic of the solvent is unlikely. Usanovich [8] has shown the similarity in electrical conductivity of solutions of such acids as the arsenic and antimony trichlorides in ether to a solution of sulfuric acid in ether. The conductance of the solutions is greater if the ether is replaced by a stronger base like pyridine. Arsenic trichloride reacts with pyridine with liberation of a large amount of heat, forming after evaporation of the excess pyridine a crystalline compound $C_5H_5N:AsCl_3$. It is a familiar fact that pyridine forms crystalline compounds with those compounds which, according to Lewis's theory, are fairly strong acids, e.g., zinc chloride. In these examples ionization of the solvent is impossible. The reaction may be represented as follows:

$$C_5H_5N: + AsCl_3 \rightleftarrows C_5H_5N:AsCl_3 \rightleftarrows C_5H_5N:AsCl_2{}^{+1} + Cl^{-1}$$

The arsenic atom becomes more negative by gaining a share in the lone electron pair of the nitrogen atom. The resulting electrical strain can be relieved by the ionization of a chlorine atom. A similar situation holds for ether.[3] An oxonium salt is formed in solution. If we regard the ether and pyridine as solvents, we see that no cation characteristic of the solvent is formed.

We might have drawn the same conclusion from the previously considered reaction between pyridine and water:

$$C_5H_5N: + HOH \rightleftarrows C_5H_5N:H^{+1} + OH^{-1}$$

If pyridine is considered the basic solvent and water the acid dissolved in it, there is again no splitting of the solvent to give a

---

[6] Jander and Mesech, *Z. physik. Chem.*, **A183**, 255, 277 (1939); also preceding papers in this series.

[7] Smith, *Chem. Revs.*, **23**, 165 (1938).

[8] Usanovich, *J. Gen. Chem. U.S.S.R.*, **9**, 182 (1939).

cation characteristic of the solvent. The above examples illustrate the inadequacy of the idea that acids and bases can be defined in terms of ions. In certain solvents, acids increase the concentration of solvent cations and bases increase the concentration of solvent anions, but in other solvents they do not. These experimental facts do not affect the electronic theory of acids and bases because it is not stated in terms of ions.

3. Typical Reactions of Acids and Bases.

Typical properties of acids and bases are usually taken to be those that are observed in water solutions of acids and bases. Most of them are due to the increased concentration of solvent cation or solvent anion caused by the presence of the acid or base. The most familiar reactions dependent upon this effect probably are the reactions between the free elements and solutions of acids and bases; electrolysis; and the reactions of amphoteric substances. The first is the only one that requires further discussion before similar reactions in other solvents are considered.

Active metals like sodium and calcium react with pure water. Active non-metals like chlorine and sulfur also react with water, but the reactions are more complex. Chlorine reacts to give hydrochloric and hypochlorous acids. Sulfur reacts slowly, when heated with water, to give several products. These reactions may be considered due to the presence of hydrogen ions and hydroxide ions. The hydrogen ions oxidize active metals and become free hydrogen. The reaction of hydroxide ions with active non-metals is not so simple. This is probably due to the fact that the oxygen atom has a greater attraction for electrons than any other atom except fluorine. Many metals will reduce hydrogen ion, but only one non-metal, fluorine, will oxidize hydroxide ion under ordinary circumstances. Chlorine and sulfur are unable to remove electrons completely from the hydroxide ion.

These reactions proceed much more rapidly when the hydrogen-ion or hydroxide-ion concentration is increased by the addition of an acid or base. The increase in rate seems to be a mass action effect, e.g., in the reaction

$$Mg + 2H^{+1} \rightarrow Mg^{+2} + H_2$$

increasing the concentration of the hydrogen ion will have the same effect whether it is done "directly" by adding hydrogen chloride or "indirectly" by adding sulfur trioxide to the water.

In like manner, it makes no difference how the hydroxide-ion concentration is increased. It may be brought about by adding the ions directly through the addition of sodium hydroxide or it may be done indirectly by adding triethylamine to the water:

$$(C_2H_5)_3N: + HOH \rightleftarrows (C_2H_5)_3N:H^{+1} + OH^{-1}$$

It is worth noting at this point that, in these typical reactions with metals (discussed further in Chapter 4), hydrogen ion and hydroxide ion are not acting strictly as acid and base, respectively. The hydrogen ion acts as an oxidizing agent, removing electrons completely from the metals that react with it. The hydroxide ion acts as a reducing agent toward the only element capable of removing electrons from it:

$$2F_2 + 4OH^{-1} \rightarrow 4F^{-1} + O_2 + 2H_2O$$

Such reactions, as well as those of electrolysis and of amphoteric behavior, have been observed in other solvents. Reactions that occur in ammonia, sulfur dioxide, acetic acid, hydrogen sulfide, hydrogen fluoride, phosgene, selenium oxychloride, alcohols, and sulfuric acid are analogous to those that take place in water. Some of them have been interpreted according to the solvent-systems theory; others, according to the proton theory. All of them may be understood more clearly on the basis of the electronic theory of acids and bases. Only a few examples will be discussed here.

A solution of aluminum chloride in phosgene dissolves metals with the liberation of carbon monoxide.[4] According to Lewis's theory, the aluminum chloride is an acid and accepts an electron pair from the solvent. The resulting electrical "strain" favors the ionization which increases the concentration of solvent cation. The solvent cation oxidizes the metal, and carbon monoxide is produced

$$COCl^{+1} + Ca \rightarrow CO + Cl^{-1} + Ca^{+2}$$

or

$$CO(AlCl_4)_2 + Ca \rightarrow CO + Ca(AlCl_4)_2$$

This behavior is analogous to that of sulfur trioxide when dissolved in water. The sulfur trioxide accepts an electron pair from the solvent, and the concentration of the solvent cation is greatly increased. The solvent *cation* oxidizes the metal, and hydrogen is produced.

Similar reactions are observed in the other solvents listed above. Those in selenium oxychloride are particularly interesting since, as with phosgene, no protons are involved. Although the reported value of its solvent conductance[9] seems to be too high, the ion concentrations in pure selenium oxychloride are likely to be relatively great. When an acid like stannic chloride is dissolved in selenium oxychloride, the result is as expected. The solution reacts more vigorously with metals than the pure solvent does because of the increased concentration of solvent cation:

$$SnCl_4 + 2SeOCl_2 \rightarrow (SeOCl^{+1})_2, SnCl_6^{-2}$$

A similar effect has not yet been investigated in sulfur dioxide. One would expect that the same behavior would be observed. Sulfur monoxide should be produced when metals react with acid solutions of sulfur dioxide. One method of preparing sulfur monoxide is by the action of thionyl chloride on metals.[10] The reactions occur at high temperatures (100° C. or above) and may be compared with the displacement of hydrogen from water by hot iron. At lower temperatures it is necessary to add acids (e.g., either sulfur trioxide or sulfuric acid) to the water before the iron will displace hydrogen from it. In the same way, we may venture to predict that sulfur monoxide will be displaced by metals from thionyl chloride at much lower temperatures if strong acids such as sulfur trioxide and boron trifluoride are added first.[11a]

The simplified notation (ignoring solvation and stages of ionization) for the dissociation of such solvents emphasizes the similarity in their reactions with metals:

$$HOH \rightleftarrows H^{+1} + OH^{-1} \quad (H_2 \text{ evolved})$$

$$COCl_2 \rightleftarrows CO^{+2} + 2Cl^{-1} \quad (CO \text{ evolved})$$

$$SOCl_2 \rightleftarrows SO^{+2} + 2Cl^{-1} \quad (\text{evolution of SO predicted})$$

Corresponding reactions for bases, i.e., the action of the solvent anion as a reducing agent, are observed in liquid ammonia. Whereas, in water, fluorine is the only active non-metal which can oxidize hydroxide ion, in ammonia the other halogens can oxidize the

[9] Julien, *J. Am. Chem. Soc.*, **47**, 1799 (1925).

[10] Schenk and Platz, *Z. anorg. Chem.*, **215**, 113 (1933).

[11] Work to test these predictions will be undertaken soon.

[11a] Note added to second edition: This prediction has been confirmed. See Hubbard and Luder, *J. Am. Chem. Soc.*, **73**, 1327 (1951).

amide ion. Iodine reacts with amide ion, just as fluorine reacts with hydroxide ion :[12]

$$3I_2 + 6NH_2{}^{-1} \rightarrow 6I^{-1} + N_2 + 4NH_3$$

The reaction is more vigorous in a solution of potassium amide in ammonia than in ammonia alone. Other reactions with non-metals like sulfur, involving an increased concentration of solvent anion, are more complex. They are similar to those in water, since, like the hydroxide ion, the amide ion does not readily lose electrons completely.

When electrolysis reactions in various solvents are considered, the conditions that determine which ion is to be discharged at either electrode are such that no definite conclusions can be drawn with regard to acid-base phenomena. For example, hydrogen is discharged at the cathode when an aqueous solution of an acid is electrolyzed, but hydrogen is also produced when an aqueous solution of sodium sulfate or of sodium hydroxide is electrolyzed. The most that can be said for the results of electrolysis is that they are consistent with what has just been said concerning cations and anions characteristic of the solvent. Carbon monoxide is discharged at the cathode when a solution of aluminum chloride in phosgene is electrolyzed. Selenium dioxide and selenium monochloride are produced at the cathode upon electrolysis of a solution of stannic chloride in selenium oxychloride.

Interpretation of the work of Bagster and Cooling [13] according to the electronic theory of acids and bases would indicate the possibility that they unknowingly produced sulfur monoxide by electrolysis. Their interest in demonstrating the existence of the hydronium ion apparently caused them to overlook indications which might have led to the discovery of sulfur monoxide. When water was added to liquid sulfur dioxide and gaseous hydrogen bromide was passed in, two liquid layers were formed. Electrolysis of the sulfur dioxide layer yielded hydrogen at the cathode and bromine at the anode. Water collected at the cathode in proportion to the amount of silver deposited in a coulometer, but the amount of hydrogen discharged was less than expected, if the only ion being discharged was the H_3O^{+1} ion. These facts indicate that hydrated SO^{+2} ions were being discharged as well as hydronium ions. Bagster and Cooling were not able to account for the

---

[12] Bergstrom, *J. Phys. Chem.*, **30**, 12 (1926).
[13] Bagster and Cooling, *J. Chem. Soc.*, **117**, 693 (1920).

smaller amount of hydrogen, but they did siphon off the sulfur dioxide layer from the water layer and try electrolysis of the sulfur dioxide alone. The conductance fell rapidly, and sulfur was deposited at the cathode, but no water. This behavior seems to indicate that the (solvated) SO^{+2} ion was being discharged to form sulfur monoxide. Sulfur monoxide decomposes readily to form sulfur and sulfur dioxide.

Amphoteric reactions such as those of the hydroxides of aluminum and zinc also occur in other solvents. When potassium hydroxide is added to insoluble aluminum hydroxide in water, the following reaction takes place:

$$
\begin{array}{c}
\text{H} \\
\text{O} \\
| \\
\text{HO—Al} \\
| \\
\text{O} \\
\text{H}
\end{array}
+ \ :\overset{\cdot\cdot}{\underset{\cdot\cdot}{\text{O}}}\text{:H}^{-1} \rightarrow
\left[
\begin{array}{c}
\text{H} \\
\text{O} \\
| \\
\text{HO—Al—OH} \\
| \\
\text{O} \\
\text{H}
\end{array}
\right]^{-1}
$$

The $Al(OH)_4{}^{-1}$ ion is soluble. It is formed because the aluminum hydroxide is acidic, in that the aluminum atom accepts an electron pair to fill its empty p orbital. An analogous reaction takes place in liquid ammonia, when insoluble aluminum amide is dissolved by potassium amide:

$$Al(NH_2)_3 + NH_2{}^{-1} \rightarrow Al(NH_2)_4{}^{-1}$$

The zinc ion is also a fairly strong acid, and its insoluble compounds with solvent anions are often amphoteric. For example, in water, liquid ammonia,[14] and glacial acetic acid [15] the following reactions occur:

$$Zn(OH)_2 + 2OH^{-1} \rightarrow Zn(OH)_4{}^{-2} \quad \text{(in water)}$$

$$Zn(NH_2)_2 + 2NH_2{}^{-1} \rightarrow Zn(NH_2)_4{}^{-2} \quad \text{(in ammonia)}$$

$$Zn(C_2H_3O_2)_2 + 2C_2H_3O_2{}^{-1} \rightarrow Zn(C_2H_3O_2)_4{}^{-2} \quad \text{(in acetic acid)}$$

All the complex anions formed are soluble. Such reactions occur because zinc and aluminum ions are fairly strong acids, having considerable tendency to fill their empty orbitals.

[14] Franklin, *The Nitrogen System of Compounds*, Reinhold Publishing Corporation, New York, 1935.
[15] Davidson, *Chem. Revs.*, **8**, 175 (1931).

All the reactions so far discussed in this section have involved amphoteric solvents which, it is assumed, may ionize. Most of the reactions involve the same effect of acids and bases on the concentration of solvent cations or solvent anions that is observed in water. They are "typical" reactions only because they resemble those in water, with which we are more familiar. We would expect, therefore, that acid-base properties in "inert" solvents such as benzene, or in non-amphoteric solvents like pyridine, would not be "typical." In these solvents, there is no possibility of a "typical" increase in solvent cations or anions upon the addition of acids or bases. Ions are produced when acids and bases react with non-amphoteric solvents like pyridine and ether, but the ions formed are not "characteristic" of the solvent.

As a rule, no ions are produced when acids and bases are dissolved in relatively inert solvents such as benzene. The assumption of "protective coatings" to explain the absence of a reaction between metals and a solution of hydrogen chloride in benzene is unnecessary. In water, metals react more rapidly when an acid is present because of the increased concentration of solvent cations. The metal reacts slowly with water, even in the absence of the acid, but no such reaction takes place in benzene because there are no solvent cations with which the metal can react. The statement is sometimes made that acids dissolved in inert solvents do not react with carbonates. But the reaction with carbonates is one that does not necessarily depend on solvent cations. It depends on the strength of the acid required to displace the weaker acid, carbon dioxide, from its compound. Lewis [1] has shown that a strong acid like boron trichloride will displace carbon dioxide from sodium carbonate in a mixture of carbon tetrachloride and acetone.

The fact that acids are not usually ionized in inert solvents permits a better determination of their relative strengths than is possible in water. In water, perchloric, hydriodic, hydrobromic, hydrochloric, and nitric acids are all practically 100 per cent ionized, thus appearing to be of equal strength. They all have such a strong tendency to accept an electron pair that the reaction with water goes to completion. Because of this "leveling effect," as Hantzsch called it, there can be no stronger acid than hydrogen ion in water. Any acid much stronger than hydrogen ion will displace it completely. One way in which the strengths of such acids can be compared is by measuring them in some inert solvent.

This has been done by Hantzsch,[16] who found a great difference in the strengths of several strong hydrogen acids. Perchloric acid is the strongest, followed in order by hydriodic, hydrobromic, hydrochloric, and nitric acids.

We have seen that Walden's fears that Lewis would deliberately eliminate the important part played by the solvent in acid-base properties were groundless. Lewis's acids and bases, dissolved in suitable amphoteric solvents, have the "typical" properties of acids and bases. These "typical" properties are the properties with which we are familiar from our study of water chemistry. Now that we are beginning to branch out into other fields, we may expect to find increasingly that the electronic theory of acids and bases is the only one so far proposed that is at all adequate.

4. The Extent of Acid-Base Phenomena.

The measure of correlation to be effected by the electronic theory of acids and bases can be surmised by recalling that all the substances that Sidgwick [3] called electron-pair acceptors and donors are really acids and bases. There is no need for any other name for them. The list of bases compiled by Brønsted and his followers is identical as far as it goes with that of Lewis, but their list of acids is limited because of their insistence upon the criterion of proton exchange. "To restrict the group of acids to those substances which contain hydrogen interferes as seriously with the systematic understanding of chemistry as would the restriction of the term oxidizing agent to substances containing oxygen." [1] There is little doubt that the recognition of acids as electron-pair acceptors and bases as electron-pair donors will lead to as great a degree of systematization as did the recognition of oxidizing agents as electron acceptors and reducing agents as electron donors. Furthermore, the possibility of correlating the two types of phenomena now appears for the first time. This correlation will be attempted in the next chapter.

The rapid growth of the list of basic substances evident since the advent of the Brønsted theory has already made acceptable to most chemists the idea that almost any atom or group of atoms may act as a base if a strong enough acid is used. The electronic theory supplies the explanation. Most atomic groupings are surrounded by some lone pairs of electrons which can be utilized by

[16] Hantzsch, Z. physik. Chem., **134**, 406 (1928).

a sufficiently strong acid to form a coordinate bond. Even the "inert" gases can act as bases by donating one or more pairs of their outer octets to strong acids. Booth and Wilson,[17] who demonstrated the existence of the boron trifluoride compounds with argon, suggested that more stable compounds would be obtained with krypton and xenon. Lewis[1] also suggests that, since sulfur trioxide is in general a stronger acid than boron fluoride, even more stable addition compounds will be formed between sulfur trioxide and the "inert" gases.

The list of substances which can behave as acids is perhaps not quite so extensive, but for practical purposes can be regarded so. Hundreds of compounds may act as acids by accepting shares in electron pairs even though they already have eight bonding electrons. Two examples of such acids are stannic chloride and silicon tetrafluoride:

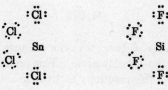

which form ions:

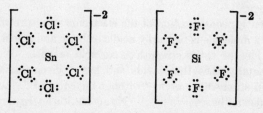

In some ways we might think of acidic or basic tendencies as being due to the properties of atoms themselves, but this idea may be misleading, as the following example shows. Sulfur trioxide is a strong acid because in it the sulfur atom has a great tendency to accept an electron pair, but the sulfide ion is a fairly strong base. Davy was not so far from the truth when he said that acidity does not depend upon a particular element, but upon the arrangement of atoms.

[17] Booth and Wilson, *J. Am. Chem. Soc.*, **57**, 2273 (1935). Note added to second edition: The existence of addition compounds of argon with boron fluoride has been disputed. See Wiberg and Karbe, *Z. anorg. Chem.*, **256**, 307 (1948).

The two preceding paragraphs have implied that many substances may act either as acids or as bases, depending upon the
particular reaction under consideration. Amphoteric behavior
seems to be much more widespread than was previously supposed.
Aluminum hydroxide

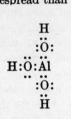

is obviously amphoteric because the aluminum atom can accept a
share in an electron pair from a base, or the hydroxyl radicals can
donate a share in one of their electron pairs to an acid. But even
strong acids like hydrogen chloride must also be considered amphoteric from the electronic viewpoint. The electronic formula

$$H:\overset{\cdot\cdot}{\underset{\cdot\cdot}{Cl}}:$$

shows the possibility of basic behavior because of the three lone
electron pairs on the chlorine atom. This prediction is borne out
experimentally by the reactions of hydrogen chloride with the
strong acids sulfur trioxide and stannic chloride to form addition
compounds.[18]

Frequently, consideration of the electronic structure will reveal
whether a molecule is primarily acidic or basic and sometimes will
give an idea as to its strength as an acid or base. It is found
experimentally that these acids and bases, given sufficient difference in strength, combine "without impediment." Lewis calls
such acids and bases *primary*.[1] No activation energy is required
for the neutralization of a primary acid by a primary base. On
the other hand, certain substances that experimentally behave
like acids, e.g., carbon dioxide and organic acid halides, have electronic formulas which, as usually written, do not show the possibility of their acting as electron-pair acceptors. Such acids and
bases are called *secondary* by Lewis. Neutralization of some of
these substances is measurably slow. Their neutralization apparently requires activation energy. Lewis suggests that such

[18] Sisler and Audrieth, *J. Am. Chem. Soc.*, **61**, 3392 (1939).

secondary acids and bases are not acids or bases in their normal
states of lowest energy, as represented by the electronic formulas
usually written, but may become acids and bases through
activation. These substances act like acids and bases, except
that their neutralization is slow, but their electronic formulas do
not indicate such behavior. Perhaps some of the difficulty
lies in the formulas.

It has been known for some time that the properties of the
carbon-oxygen double bond are not well represented by the usual
formula. Lowry suggested in 1923 that, instead of representing
the carbonyl group as

$$R_2C::\overset{..}{\underset{}{O}}:$$

the formula

$$\overset{(+)}{R_2}\overset{}{C}:\overset{..}{\underset{..}{O}}:\overset{(-)}{}$$

should be used. (The plus and minus signs in parentheses indicate electrical dissymmetry; they are not intended to represent
unit charge or to indicate valence.) Since the carbon atom in the
second formula has only six electrons the possibility of acidic behavior is indicated. Basic behavior should be evident also through
the electron pairs on the oxygen. Compounds containing such
groups should be amphoteric. The familiar addition reactions of
aldehydes confirm this conclusion. The first step in such reactions
can be represented by the following equations:

$$
\begin{array}{ccc}
\text{H} & :\overset{..}{\underset{}{Cl}}: & \text{H} \quad :\overset{..}{\underset{}{Cl}}: \\
R:\overset{..}{\underset{..}{C}}:\overset{..}{\underset{..}{O}}: + \overset{..}{Al}:\overset{..}{\underset{..}{Cl}}: & \rightarrow & R:\overset{..}{\underset{..}{C}}:\overset{..}{\underset{..}{O}}:\overset{..}{Al}:\overset{..}{\underset{..}{Cl}}: \\
& :\overset{}{\underset{..}{Cl}}: & \quad\quad :\overset{}{\underset{..}{Cl}}: \\
\text{base} & \text{acid} &
\end{array}
$$

$$
\begin{array}{cccc}
\text{H} & \text{H} & \text{H} & \text{H} \\
R:\overset{}{\underset{}{C}} + & :\overset{..}{\underset{..}{N}}:\text{H} & \rightarrow \quad R:\overset{}{\underset{}{C}} & : \quad \overset{}{\underset{}{N}}:\text{H} \\
:\overset{}{\underset{..}{O}}: & \overset{}{\underset{}{H}} & :\overset{}{\underset{..}{O}}: & \overset{}{\underset{}{H}} \\
\text{acid} & \text{base} & &
\end{array}
$$

The acid halides exhibit more definite "typical" acidic behavior in
one respect, because they can react with water to increase the concentration of hydrogen ions:

$$\underset{\text{acid}}{R-\overset{..}{\underset{..}{\overset{:\overset{..}{O}:}{C}}}+}\quad \underset{\text{base}}{:\overset{..}{\underset{..}{O}}:H} \rightarrow R-\overset{:\overset{..}{Cl}:H}{\underset{:\overset{..}{O}:}{\overset{..}{C}:\overset{..}{O}:H}} \rightarrow R:C:\overset{..}{\underset{:\overset{..}{O}:}{O}}:H + H^{+1} + :\overset{..}{\underset{..}{Cl}}:^{-1}$$

$$\downarrow$$

$$R:C:\overset{..}{\underset{:\overset{..}{O}}{O}}:H$$

Carbon dioxide is another example of a "secondary" acid. Assuming that the activated molecule can be represented by a formula similar to that just used for the carbonyl group, the reaction between carbon dioxide and water could be written:

$$\overset{:\overset{..}{O}:}{\underset{:\overset{..}{O}:}{C}} + :\overset{..}{O}:H \leftrightarrows \overset{:\overset{..}{O}:}{\underset{:\overset{..}{O}}{C}}:\overset{..}{O}:H \leftrightarrows \left[\overset{:\overset{..}{O}:}{\underset{:\overset{..}{O}:}{C}}:\overset{..}{O}:H \right]^{-1} + H^{+1}$$

Another type of "secondary" behavior is evident when amphoteric molecules partially or wholly neutralize each other, or when molecules are neutralized by the solvent in which they are placed. For example, the acid A may be dissolved in the weak base B and be neutralized, in that the stable electron configuration of the acidic atom has been attained by acceptance of electron pairs from the base. Yet, if a stronger base B^1 is added, the stronger base will replace the weaker one in combination with the acid:

$$B^1 + AB \rightarrow AB^1 + B$$

Such reactions will be discussed in greater detail in Chapter 8. They usually require activation, but in many reactions the activation energy is small enough to be ignored. This seems to be true of the reactions of strong hydrogen acids such as HCl.

Another extension of the idea of acids and bases involves acidic and basic radicals in organic compounds. For example, the familiar *ortho-para*-directing groups for substitutions in the benzene ring are basic. They have electron pairs that they can share with a neighboring atom. The *meta*-directing groups are acidic. They can share an electron pair possessed by a neighboring atom.

The action of the acid and basic radicals in directing substituents will be considered in Chapter 5.

Many compounds which at first glance seem to offer no possibility of behaving as acids or bases may be forced to do so by reaction with strong bases or acids. For example, in the sulfonation of benzene by sulfur trioxide, the simplest explanation would seem to be that the SO_3 molecule coordinates with two of the electrons from the benzene molecule as follows:

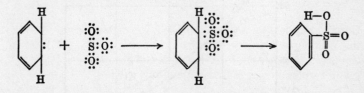

Thus a very strong acid can force even benzene to behave as a base. Similar behavior induced by other strong acids like aluminum chloride and boron trifluoride can be postulated to clear up a great deal of the mystery which until quite recently surrounded catalysis of the type observed in Friedel-Crafts reactions. This kind of catalysis will be dealt with in the concluding chapters.

One striking illustration of the simplification of chemistry made possible by the Lewis theory occurs in the hydrolysis of salts. According to the electronic theory, any sufficiently strong acid or base will increase the concentration of cation or anion in an ionizing solvent. When a test with litmus shows a salt solution to be acidic or basic, a single simple equation is often all that is necessary by way of explanation. For example, the hydrolysis of zinc chloride may be represented by the equation

$$Zn^{+2} + HOH \rightarrow ZnOH^{+1} + H^{+1}$$

The explanation is simply that the zinc ion in zinc chloride is acidic.

The solubility of some salts in pyridine and other amines of low dielectric constant is more readily understood in terms of acid-base behavior. The metallic ion, being acidic, coordinates molecules of solvent about it. Silver salts in pyridine, ethylenediamine,[19] and other amines [20] show "abnormal" conductance curves.

[19] Bromley and Luder, *J. Am. Chem. Soc.*, **66**, 107 (1944).
[20] Elsey, *J. Am. Chem. Soc.*, **42**, 2454 (1920).

A possible explanation lies in the fact that the silver ion is a fairly strong acid. For example, Bromley and Luder [19] measured the conductance of potassium iodide, silver nitrate, and silver iodide in ethylenediamine. It was hoped that potassium nitrate could

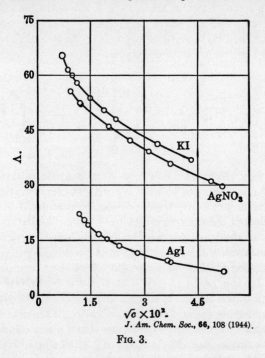

J. Am. Chem. Soc., **66**, 108 (1944).

FIG. 3.

also be measured to permit comparison of Λ_0 values, but it proved too insoluble. Figure 3 and Table 1 summarize the data (a is the "ion size").

TABLE 1

SALT	Λ_0	$K \times 10^4$	$a \times 10^8$
Kl	69.2	6.02	5.34
AgNO₃	61.4	8.07	5.98
AgI	48.8	0.431	3.84 *

* This value has little meaning, since other than coulomb forces are involved.

It is not surprising that the solubility of potassium nitrate is too low for conductance measurements. The potassium ion has very little tendency to coordinate with bases. Silver nitrate (because of the acidic silver ion) and potassium iodide (because of the amphoteric nature of the iodide ion [21]) behave about as expected. Both the silver and the iodide ions are probably solvated by the highly basic solvent. "Normal" conductance behavior is observed in that greater ion size as indicated by lower Λ_0 is associated with a larger value of K (Table 1).

At first glance, the behavior of silver iodide seems rather surprising. The low Λ_0 value indicates larger ions, as would be expected, since both ions should be solvated rather than only one, as in potassium iodide and silver nitrate. But K, instead of being larger, is actually only about one-fifteenth the values for the other two salts. The explanation may lie in the fact that the model, upon which the expectation of a high K value accompanying low mobility is based, assumes only the presence of coulomb forces between the ions.[22] In silver iodide additional forces are present which make K less than predicted when coulomb forces alone are involved. These forces are of the acid-base type. The amphoteric nature of the iodide ion is beginning to be appreciated and is here substantiated. The results for silver nitrate and potassium iodide indicate that both silver and iodide ions are acting as acids in their association with the highly basic solvent. But toward the acidic silver ion the iodide ion acts as a base, tending to donate a pair of electrons to give covalent character to the bond between the two ions. The presence of these additional forces decreases K to a value far below that expected from the low value of Λ_0. This conclusion is supported by the fact that, although AgCl and AgBr crystallize in ionic lattices, crystalline AgI has the zinc blende structure, in which the atoms are held together by covalent bonds.[23]

Tables 2 and 3 summarize some of the simpler fundamentals of the electronic theory of acids and bases.

[21] The basic nature of the iodide ion has long been accepted by followers of Brønsted. The acidic nature of the iodide ion is due to its ability to take on additional electron pairs. The ion itself contains only eight electrons, but the iodine atom is capable of holding more valence electrons, as shown by the formulas of the covalent compounds ICl_5 and IF_7 discussed in Chapter 2. Additional information on this point may be obtained from the review by R. B. Sandin (*Chem. Revs.*, **32**, 249 [1943]).

[22] Fuoss and Kraus, *J. Am. Chem. Soc.*, **55**, 1019 (1933).

[23] Palmer, *Valency: Classical and Modern*, Cambridge University Press, Cambridge, England, 1944.

TABLE 2

ACID-BASE REACTIONS IN GENERAL

(H^{+1} used for simplicity)

Description	Acid	Base	Product
Neutralization			
The water definition is a special case.	H^{+1}	OH^{-1}	HOH
The solvent-systems definition is a special case.	(COCl)$^{+1}$	Cl^{-1}	COCl$_2$
The Brønsted definition is a special case.	HCl	NH$_3$	NH$_4$Cl
The electronic theory includes all three.	Electron-pair acceptor	Electron-pair donor	Neutralization—formation of a coordinate bond
And many others, e.g.	BCl$_3$	(C$_2$H$_5$)$_3$N	(C$_2$H$_5$)$_3$N→BCl$_3$
	AlCl$_3$	(C$_5$H$_5$)$_2$O	(C$_5$H$_5$)$_2$O→AlCl$_3$
	SO$_3$	C$_5$H$_5$N	C$_5$H$_5$N→SO$_3$
	CO$_2$	CaO	CaCO$_3$
	Ca^{+2}	OH^{-1}	Ca(OH)$_2$
	Ag^{+1}	NH$_3$	Ag(NH$_3$)$_2$$^{+1}$
Displacement			
A strong acid may displace a weaker one from combination with a base.	BCl$_3$	Na$_2$CO$_3$	CO$_2$ + [Na$_2$O→BCl$_3$]
	H^{+1}	Al(OH)$_3$	Al^{+3} + HOH
	H^{+1}	Cu(NH$_3$)$_4$$^{+2}$	Cu^{+2} + NH$_4$$^{+1}$
A strong base may displace a weaker one from combination with an acid.	C$_5$H$_5$N→SO$_3$	NH$_3$	C$_5$H$_5$N + [H$_3$N→SO$_3$]
	HC$_2$H$_3$O$_2$	OH^{-1}	C$_2$H$_3$O$_2$$^{-1}$ + HOH
	NH$_4$$^{+1}$	OH^{-1}	NH$_3$ + HOH
Catalysis			
Many acids catalyze organic reactions.	AlCl$_3$, BF$_3$, HF, SO$_3$		
Bases also catalyze organic reactions.	E.g., reaction between alcohols and benzoyl chloride more rapid in pyridine		
The presence of acids increases speed of reaction of ionizing solvents with metals.	Acid increases concentration of solvent cations SO$_3$ + HOH→H^{+1} + HSO$_4$$^{-1}$; AlCl$_3$ + COCl$_2$→COCl^{+1} + AlCl$_4$$^{-1}$		
Bases also may speed solvent reactions similarly.	Base increases concentration of solvent anions NH$_3$ + HOH→OH^{-1} + NH$_4$$^{+1}$; (C$_2H_5$)$_3$N + COCl$_2$→(C$_2H_5$)$_3$NCOCl^{+1} + Cl^{-1}		

TABLE 3

ACID-BASE REACTIONS IN IONIZING SOLVENTS

(Hydration of the solvent cation usually not shown)

Description	Acid	Base	Product
Ionization			
According to the theory of solvent systems	$AlCl_3$	$COCl_2$	$COCl^{+1} + AlCl_4^{-1}$
According to the Brønsted theory	HCl	HOH	$H_3O^{+1} + Cl^{-1}$
Both are special cases of the electronic theory.	Electron-pair acceptor	Electron-pair donor	Coordinate bond formation involving ionization
Other examples: (s denotes solvent.) Note that an acid reacting with an ionizing solvent increases the concentration of solvent cations; a base increases the anion concentration.	CO_2	HOH (s)	$H^{+1} + HCO_3^{-1}$
	HOH (s)	NH_3	$OH^{-1} + NH_4^{+1}$
	HOH (s)	C_5H_5N	$OH^{-1} + C_5H_5NH^{+1}$
	BCl_3	$SeOCl_2$ (s)	$SeOCl^{+1} + BCl_4^{-1}$
	$SeOCl_2$ (s)	$(C_2H_5)_3N$	$Cl^{-1} + (C_2H_5)_3NSeOCl^{+1}$
Hydrolysis of Salts			
Reaction of cation acid with solvent (when anion is weak base, e.g., Cl^{-1}	NH_4^{+1}	HOH	$H_3O^{+1} + NH_3$
	Zn^{+2}	HOH	$H^{+1} + ZnOH^{+1}$
Reaction of anion base with solvent (when cation is weak acid, e.g., Na^{+1}	HOH	CN^{-1}	$OH^{-1} + HCN$
	HOH	CO_3^{-2}	$OH^{-1} + HCO_3^{-1}$
Amphoteric Behavior			
Water is amphoteric (it can donate or accept an electron pair).	HOH	NH_3	$NH_4^{+1} + OH^{-1}$
	HCl	HOH	$H_3O^{+1} + Cl^{-1}$
Aluminum hydroxide is amphoteric (donates or accepts an electron pair).	$Al(OH)_3$	OH^{-1}	$Al(OH)_4^{-1}$
	H^{+1}	$Al(OH)_3$	$Al^{+3} + HOH$
Complex Ions			
	Ag^{+1}	CN^{-1}	$Ag(CN)_2^{-1}$
	Cu^{+2}	NH_3	$Cu(NH_3)_4^{+2}$
	$SnCl_4$	Cl^{-1}	$SnCl_6^{-2}$
	As_2S_5	S^{-2}	AsS_4^{-3}

Although consistent application of the electronic theory of acids and bases simplifies and systematizes a great deal of chemistry, the amount of correlation can be increased still further by developing the relationship between acids and bases on the one hand and oxidizing and reducing agents on the other. This will be done in the following chapter.

Chapter 4

ELECTROPHILIC AND ELECTRODOTIC REAGENTS

1. The Resemblance of Oxidation-Reduction to Acid-Base Reactions.

The experimental relationship between acids and oxidizing agents is a close one. In fact, as has been pointed out in Chapter 3, the "typical" effect of an acid solution on metals is due to the oxidizing action of the solvent cation; for example:

and

$$Mg + 2H^{+1} \rightarrow Mg^{+2} + H_2 \quad \text{(in water)}$$

$$Ca + CO^{+2} \rightarrow Ca^{+2} + CO \quad \text{(in phosgene)}$$

The acidic cation of the solvent in this particular type of reaction is behaving not as an acid but as an oxidizing agent. The action of basic anions upon non-metals (already referred to) is comparable. Hydroxide ions in water, and amide ions in liquid ammonia, reduce active non-metals, for example:

$$2F_2 + 4OH^{-1} \rightarrow 4F^{-1} + O_2 + 2H_2O \quad \text{(in water)}$$

and

$$3I_2 + 6NH_2^{-1} \rightarrow 6I^{-1} + N_2 + 4NH_3 \quad \text{(in ammonia)}$$

These experimental data show the close relationship between acids and oxidizing agents on the one hand and bases and reducing agents on the other, but occasionally a comparison has been attempted which, at first glance, seems to lead to an opposite conclusion.

A formal analogy is worked out as follows: A reducing agent is an electron donor. An acid is a proton donor. An acid, therefore, resembles a reductant in that both are donors. An acid cannot donate protons unless a base is present, nor can a reducing agent donate electrons unless an oxidizing agent is present to accept them. Both types of reactions are mutual affairs between the acid and the base, or between the oxidant and the reductant. For example, the equation

$$\overbrace{Zn^{\circ} + Cu}^{2e}{}^{+2} \rightleftarrows Zn^{+2} + Cu^{\circ}$$

reductant₁   oxidant₂   oxidant₁   reductant₂

is similar to the type equation of the Brønsted theory:

$$\overbrace{HCl + H_2O}^{1p} \rightleftarrows H_3O^{+1} + Cl^{-1}$$

acid₁   base₂   acid₂   base₁

This mutuality is regarded as a confirmation of the analogy.

Actually the analogy between the two equations depends upon the fact that the typical acid-base reaction of the Brønsted theory represents only one of the four experimental criteria of acid-base phenomena—displacement. (Displacement will be considered in detail in Chapter 8.) The whole analogy is only a formal comparison, and, of course, its advocates do not claim that it shows any definite relationship between acid-base and oxidation-reduction reactions.

Usanovich attempted to explain the relationship by including oxidation as a special case of acidic behavior.[1] Reduction was considered a special case of basic behavior. Chlorine was listed as an acid and sodium as a base. This classification has more experimental justification than would appear at first glance. Sodium, when reacting with water, increases the concentration of solvent anions as do bases when dissolved in many amphoteric solvents:

$$2Na + 2H_2O \rightarrow 2OH^{-1} + 2Na^{+1} + H_2$$

The corresponding property of acids in amphoteric solvents, namely, the increase in solvent cation concentration, is exhibited by chlorine:

$$Cl_2 + H_2O \rightarrow 2H^{+1} + Cl^{-1} + OCl^{-1}$$

On the other hand, some oxidizing and reducing agents do not have such properties of acids and bases. For example, the permanganate ion is a strong oxidizing agent, but it is not an acid.

---

[1] Usanovich. *J. Gen. Chem. U.S.S.R.*, **9**, 182 (1939).

It seems, therefore, that a more general classification is necessary, one that will include both types of behavior.

2. Electronic Reactions.

An inclusive classification can be made by dividing the reagents that take part in acid-base and oxidation-reduction reactions into two types. Electrophilic reagents are those that gain electrons in the reaction under consideration. Electrodotic reagents are those that lose electrons in the reaction under consideration. The term *electrophilic* has been in use for some time to refer to reagents such as chlorine molecules and hydrogen ions which have an attraction for electrons. Those reagents which, like sodium, give up electrons readily have been called *nucleophilic*. *Electrophilic* seems to be a good word to retain, since it graphically describes the theoretical action of the reagents to which it applies. But *nucleophilic* is an unfortunate choice. It is difficult to picture sodium or other strong reducing agents as actually nucleophilic. A term that indicates ability to give up electrons readily is more appropriate. *Electrodomic* (Gr. *didomi*, to give) was the term originally suggested,[2] but, as pointed out by Professor N. F. Hall, *electrodotic* seems better etymologically.[3] Some reagents may be electrophilic under one set of conditions but electrodotic under another set. This double behavior is already familiar as far as acid-base phenomena are concerned; the word used to describe it is "amphoteric." For lack of a better one, we might as well use the same word to apply to oxidizing and reducing agents. When a reagent is acting as an acid or an oxidizing agent, it is electrophilic. When it is acting as a base or a reducing agent, it is electrodotic.

Primary acids and oxidizing agents are electron acceptors. An acid accepts a share in an electron pair held by a base; an oxidizing agent takes over completely the electrons donated by a reducing agent. Both are electrophilic and in many cases may act either as acids or as oxidizing agents:

$$H^{+1} + \ddot{:}\!\overset{..}{O}\!:\!H^{-1} \rightarrow H\!:\!\overset{..}{\underset{..}{O}}\!:\!H$$

acid

$$\overset{\frown{1e}}{H^{+1}} + Na \rightarrow Na^{+1} + \tfrac{1}{2}H_2$$

oxidant

[2] Luder, *Chem. Revs.*, **27**, 547 (1940).
[3] Hall, *J. Am. Chem. Soc.*, **63**, 883 (1941).

Both bases and reducing agents are electron donors. A base donates a share in an electron pair to an acid; a reducing agent loses electrons completely to an oxidizing agent. Both are electrodotic and may act either as bases or as reducing agents:

$$H:\overset{..}{\underset{..}{O}}:^{-1} + H^{+1} \rightarrow H:\overset{..}{\underset{..}{O}}:H$$
base

$$2H:\overset{..}{\underset{..}{O}}:^{-1} + F_2 \rightarrow 2F^{-1} + \tfrac{1}{2}O_2 + H_2O$$
reductant

A few reagents are listed in Table 1 according to some manifestations of their electrophilic and electrodotic tendencies. The most active oxidizing agent, fluorine, is placed at the top of the

TABLE 1

ELECTROPHILIC AND ELECTRODOTIC REAGENTS

Electrophilic Reagents: Acids and Oxidants			*Electrodotic Reagents:* Bases and Reductants		
Number of electrons accepted			Number of electrons donated		
Reagent	By sharing (Acid)	By transfer (Oxidant)	Reagent	By sharing (Base)	By transfer (Reductant)
F_2		2	Cs		1
MnO_4^{-1}		5	Sn^{+2}		2
Cl_2		2	HCl	2	1
Sn^{+2}		2	I^{-1}	2	1
H_2O	2, 4	2	$C_6H_4(OH)_2$	2, 4	2
$C_6H_4(OH)_2$	2, 4	2	$(C_2H_5)_2O$	2	?
SO_2	2, 4		C_5H_5N	2	?
Ag^{+1}	2, 4	1	H_2O	2	2
Cu^{+2}	8	1, 2	CN^{-1}	2	1
H^{+1}	2	1	NH_3	2	3
CH_3COCl	2	?	$(C_2H_5)_3N$	2	?
HCl	2		S^{-2}	2, 4, 6	2
BF_3	2		NH_2^{-1}	2	1
SO_3	2		OH^{-1}	2, 4	1

list of electrophilic reagents and one of the strongest acids, sulfur trioxide, is at the bottom. The order is roughly that of increasing acid strength downward. The list of electrodotic reagents is arranged correspondingly, with the strongest reducing agent, cesium, at the top and the strongest bases toward the bottom. Apparently some of the strongest oxidizing agents do not act as acids, nor do some of the strongest acids act as oxidizing agents. A similar relationship appears to hold for electrodotic reagents.

Discussion of a few examples from Table 1 should help to clarify its significance. As shown above, hydrogen ion acts as an acid in accepting a share in an electron pair from the hydroxide ion, but toward an active reducing agent such as sodium it behaves not as an acid but as an oxidant. Silver ion acts as an acid in accepting a pair of electrons from hydroxide ion to form silver hydroxide

$$Ag^{+1} + :\overset{..}{\underset{..}{O}}:H^{-1} \rightarrow Ag:\overset{..}{\underset{..}{O}}:H$$
$$\text{acid} \qquad \text{base}$$

which decomposes to silver oxide. It also acts as an acid in reacting with ammonia or cyanide ion to form complex ions:

$$Ag^{+1} + 2NH_3 \rightarrow Ag(NH_3)_2{}^{+1}$$
$$Ag^{+1} + 2CN^{-1} \rightarrow Ag(CN)_2{}^{-1}$$
$$\text{acid} \quad \text{base}$$

Toward reducing agents the silver ion acts not as an acid but as an oxidizing agent:

$$2Ag^{+1} + Cu^\circ \rightarrow 2Ag^\circ + Cu^{+2}$$
$$\text{oxidant} \quad \text{reductant}$$

Hydroxide ion acts as a base in sharing a pair of electrons with hydrogen ion to form water, but it acts as a reducing agent in giving up electrons to the oxidant fluorine. Amide ion behaves as a base toward ammonium ion

$$NH_2{}^{-1} + NH_4{}^{+1} \rightarrow 2NH_3$$
$$\text{base}$$

but as a reductant toward iodine:

$$6NH_2{}^{-1} + 3I_2 \rightarrow 6I^{-1} + 4NH_3 + N_2$$
$$\text{reductant}$$

Cyanide and sulfide ions react as bases toward water

$$CN^{-1} + H_2O \rightarrow HCN + OH^{-1}$$
$$S^{-2} + 2H_2O \rightarrow H_2S + 2OH^{-1}$$
$$\text{base}$$

but as reductants toward oxidizing agents. For example, the ease with which sulfide ion is oxidized by ferric ion is well known:

$$S^{-2} + 2Fe^{+3} \rightarrow S^\circ + 2Fe^{+2}$$
$$\text{reductant}$$

Iodide ion is a very weak base but does react with some acids to give stable complex ions, e.g.,

$$4I^{-1} + Hg^{+2} \rightarrow HgI_4^{-2}$$
base

On the other hand, it is a good reducing agent, being easily oxidized to free iodine:

$$2I^{-1} + Cl_2 \rightarrow 2Cl^{-1} + I_2$$
reductant

3. Amphoteric Behavior.

Four of the substances included in Table 1—water, hydrogen chloride, hydroquinone, and stannous ion—appear in both columns. This is entirely in accord with the familiar behavior of acids and bases described by the term "amphoteric." We propose to use the same term to apply to the corresponding behavior when it is encountered in oxidation-reduction reactions.

It is an experimental fact that the same substance may under properly chosen conditions act as an acid, a base, an oxidizing agent, or a reducing agent. For example, water acts as an acid toward ammonia, as a base toward sulfur dioxide, as an oxidizing agent toward active metals, and as a reducing agent toward fluorine (Table 2). Water is not only amphoteric in the usual sense but also is both an oxidizing agent and a reducing agent.[4] The same is true of many other substances besides water. Most reagents cannot be arbitrarily classified as acid or base, or as oxidizing or reducing agent. Their behavior depends upon the specific circumstances of a particular reaction. Therefore, the words electrophilic and electrodotic are relative terms, depending upon conditions. They refer to the behavior of a substance as it acts in the particular reaction under consideration.

Continuing with the other substances listed on both sides of Table 1, hydrogen chloride is ordinarily thought of as a strong acid, but it behaves as a base toward sulfur trioxide or stannic chloride (Chapter 3). On the other hand, the hydrogen ion acts

[4] Note that, as shown in Table 2, a reducing agent as well as a base may increase the concentration of solvent anions. Also an oxidizing agent as well as an acid may increase the concentration of solvent cations. Thus, according to the theory of solvent systems, sodium would be a base and fluorine an acid. This conclusion is one more illustration of the inadequacy of the idea that acids and bases can be defined in terms of ions.

as an oxidizing agent toward active metals, but the chloride ion acts as a reducing agent toward strong oxidizing agents such as permanganate.

TABLE 2

Amphoteric Behavior of Water

Electrophilic

$$H_2O + NH_3 \rightarrow OH^{-1} + NH_4^{+1}$$
acid

$$2H_2O + 2Na \rightarrow 2OH^{-1} + 2Na^{+1} + H_2$$
oxidant

Electrodotic

$$H_2O + SO_2 \rightarrow H^{+1} + HSO_3^{-1}$$
base

$$2H_2O + 2F_2 \rightarrow 4H^{+1} + 4F^{-1} + O_2$$
reductant

Hydroquinone is similar to water and hydrogen chloride in its amphoteric behavior. It can behave both as an acid toward bases and as an oxidizing agent toward reducing agents because of the presence of the labile protons. Or it may act both as a base toward acids and as a reducing agent toward oxidizing agents (particularly in water) because of the hydroquinone ion. The familiar reactions of the closely related quinone again illustrate the need for an extension of our ideas of amphoteric behavior. Quinone as an oxidizing agent is electrophilic, but as a base it is electrodotic.

Stannous ion, as far as its more familiar reactions are concerned, is amphoteric in oxidation-reduction reactions but is not in general to be thought of as amphoteric in acid-base reactions (one would expect its basic properties to be extremely weak).

These examples should be sufficient to illustrate the necessity of avoiding the idea that very many substances can be classified arbitrarily as electrophilic or electrodotic. The terms are very useful, but they are relative terms applying to a substance only as it behaves in the particular reaction under consideration.

4. Odd-Electron Molecules.

Odd-electron molecules (often called free radicals) can behave either as electrophiles or electrodotes or even as both simultaneously. Probably the outstanding examples are the triarylmethyl compounds. For example, hexaphenylethane is partially dissociated in benzene solution to give triphenylmethyl [5]

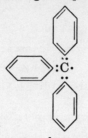

in which the central carbon atom has seven electrons. Nevertheless it is an electrically neutral molecule comparable to another odd-electron molecule, namely, nitrogen dioxide. Probably triphenylmethyl should no more be called a "free radical" than nitrogen dioxide. They are both similar in associating into double molecules and for the same reason. Each molecule has one unshared electron.

When two triarylmethyl molecules associate, each one is acting *simultaneously* as an electrophilic and as an electrodotic reagent to form a covalent bond:

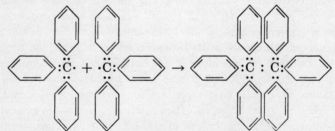

On the other hand, the triarylmethyl molecule may act as a reducing agent (an electrodote) to form a carbonium ion:

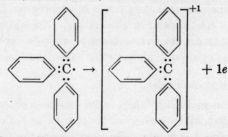

[5] Gilman, *Organic Chemistry*, John Wiley & Sons, New York, 1938.

or it may act as an oxidizing agent (an electrophile) to form a carbanion:

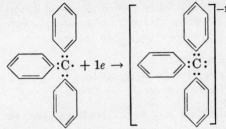

Obviously odd-electron molecules must also be classified as amphoteric.

5. Classification of Chemical Reactions.

In view of the amount of systematization and simplification in chemistry made possible through the classification of substances as electrophilic or electrodotic according to the way they behave in specific reactions, a natural question to bring up is: How does this new classification of reactions affect the older one? In the past, chemical reactions have been listed as (1) combination, (2) decomposition, (3) displacement, (4) metathesis, (5) neutralization, and (6) oxidation-reduction. This scheme has already been criticized by Hazlehurst.[6] With the Brønsted theory in mind, Hazlehurst suggests using only three types in place of the familiar six: acid-base, oxidation-reduction, combination-decomposition. His third classification seemed necessary because of the limitation by the Brønsted theory of acids and bases to proton donors and proton acceptors. For example, since the reaction

$$SO_3 + H_2O \rightarrow H_2SO_4$$

is considered neither an acid-base nor an oxidation-reduction reaction, the third classification is required. According to the Lewis theory this is an acid-base reaction. From the broader viewpoint it is apparent that most of the other reactions included in the combination-decomposition type by Hazlehurst can be assigned to either the first or second. However, there is one class of reactions which cannot be reassigned in this way, namely, reactions involving combination of odd-electron molecules or the decomposition of the product of such combination.

[6] Hazlehurst, *J. Chem. Education*, **17**, 466 (1940).

We suggest the following modifications in Hazlehurst's classification of chemical reactions: (1) broadening the first class to include all acids and bases as well as proton donors and proton acceptors; (2) limiting the third class to odd-electron-molecule reactions. The three classes then become:

I. Acid-base reactions.
II. Oxidation-reduction reactions.
III. Odd-electron-molecule reactions.

More than one class may be involved in a given reaction.

One advantage of such a classification is that, although it is based upon experimental data, it also has a simple theoretical basis. Acid-base reactions involve coordinate covalent bonds; oxidation-reduction reactions involve changes in valence; odd-electron-molecule reactions involve simple covalent bonds. The following comparison illustrates the differences between the suggested classification and the older one:

1. *Combination* may involve neutralization, oxidation, or combination of odd-electron molecules, e.g.,

$$BCl_3 + NH_3 \rightarrow [H_3N{\rightarrow}BCl_3] \quad \text{(acid-base)}$$

$$2Na + Cl_2 \rightarrow 2NaCl \quad \text{(oxidation-reduction)}$$

$$NO_2 + NO_2 \rightarrow N_2O_4 \quad \text{(odd-electron-molecule combination)}$$

2. *Decomposition* may be merely the reverse of the above reactions.

3. *Displacement* may be associated with acid-base, oxidation-reduction, or odd-electron phenomena. For example:

$$HCl + H_2O \rightarrow H_3O^{+1} + Cl^{-1} \quad \text{(acid-base)}$$

$$Zn + CuSO_4 \rightarrow ZnSO_4 + Cu \quad \text{(oxidation-reduction)}$$

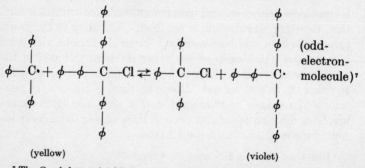

(yellow)   (violet)

[7] The Greek letter ϕ (phi) is used to represent a benzenoid ring.

(Displacement reactions involving acids and bases will be considered in Chapter 8.)

4. *Metathesis* in the usual sense, according to our present understanding of electrolytic reactions, does not occur at all. When the term was first proposed for such reactions, their true nature was not understood. The reaction which then was written

$$NaCl + AgNO_3 \rightarrow NaNO_3 + \underline{AgCl}$$

is now written

$$Ag^{+1} + Cl^{-1} \rightarrow \underline{AgCl}$$

and is usually regarded as combination. But this classification is unnecessary because the formation of a precipitate depends upon solubility. Even the "reaction"

$$Na^{+1} + Cl^{-1} \rightarrow \underline{NaCl}$$

will take place if the concentrations of the two ions in solution are high enough, for example, upon evaporation of the solvent. Evidently "metathesis" is merely a matter of solubility, not a class of chemical reactions.

Chapter 5

ACIDIC AND BASIC RADICALS

1. Introduction.

The classification of chemical substances as electrophilic and electrodotic according to their behavior in their reactions with other substances can be extended to radicals in a molecule. When this is done, a flood of light is thrown upon the nature of acid-base catalysis. Ingold,[1,2] Robinson,[3] and others have already done much to clarify many organic reaction mechanisms, but the electronic theory of acids and bases provides a measure of correlation and insight which so far is unobtainable by any other method. Generalized acid-base catalysis will be considered later. In this chapter we shall deal primarily with the effect of acidic and basic radicals in the benzene ring.

Various terms have been proposed to describe what we here call acidic and basic radicals. The principal ones are (1) electrophilic and cationoid for acid radicals and (2) nucleophilic and anionoid for basic radicals. The reasons for preferring *electrophilic* and *electrodotic* to describe general behavior have been given in the preceding chapter. In this chapter we are concerned with the specific acidic and basic nature of the radicals, so the terms *acidic* and *basic* will be used.

The electronic theory of acids and bases is very helpful in explaining the orienting effects produced by many functional groups attached to benzenoid compounds. The acidic radicals (electro-

[1] Ingold, *Chem. Revs.*, **15**, 225 (1934).

[2] Ingold, *Rec. trav. chem.*, **48**, 797 (1929).

[3] Robinson, *J. Soc. Dyers Colourists, Jubilee Journal*, **1934**, pp. 65–76.

philic or electron-withdrawal [4'] groups) are those that produce
mainly a *meta-directing* influence on subsequent ring substitutions.

$$\underset{\|}{\overset{O}{}}$$

Such groups as carbonyl (—C—), sulfo (—SO_2OH), cyano (—CN),
and nitro (—NO_2) fall in this category. The basic radicals (electrodotic or electron-release [4] groups) are those that produce mainly
an *ortho*- and *para*-directing influence. Some of these groups are
the amino (—NH_2), substituted amino (—NHR or —NR_2),
hydroxyl (—OH), and alkoxyl (—OR) groups.[5]

2. Acidic Radicals.

The acidic characteristics of these radicals are often ascribed to
displacement of an electron pair (⌣) which results in an electron
deficit on one atom (Chapter 2). This atom thus becomes acidic
(electrophilic).

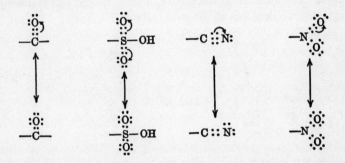

The sulfur atom in the sulfo group is also made electrophilic (to
realize its covalence maximum, as discussed in Chapter 2), by the
electron displacements (⌣) shown.

The presence of these acidic radicals in a benzenoid system
results in neutralization within the molecule. For example, the
electrophilic nitrogen of the nitro group behaves as an acid and
accepts a share in an electron pair belonging to the phenyl group.
The phenyl group thus behaves as a base by furnishing an electron
pair to the nitrogen atom.

[4] Relative to hydrogen.
[5] Gilman, *Organic Chemistry*, John Wiley & Sons, Vol. II, 1943, pp.
1845–7.

In the following formulas the unshared pairs of electrons are represented by writing a dash (for each electron pair) parallel, rather than perpendicular, to the symbol of the atom.

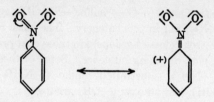

Whether or not a double bond is actually formed by this neutralization is unimportant. The acidic nitro group would, nevertheless, cause the *ortho* carbon to become electrophilic because of the resulting shift of an electron pair toward the acidic nitrogen. These electronic shifts, and those shown below, would produce low electron densities at the *ortho* and *para* carbons and relatively high electron densities at the *meta* carbons.

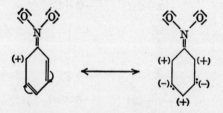

The acidic functional groups produce two main effects on the phenyl groups: (1) relatively increased electron densities at the *meta* positions, and (2) reduced overall electron density of the ring due to electron withdrawal from the ring.

3. Basic Radicals.

The basic radicals behave as bases because they contain unshared pairs of electrons which they can share with any electrophilic group. The phenyl group may behave as an "electron sink"; it can accept a share in a pair of electrons supplied by basic (electrodotic) groups.

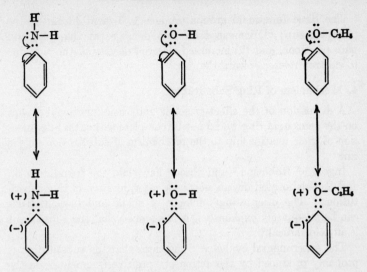

The basic groups are thus neutralized by the acidic phenyl group. The result of these electron shifts (⌣) is an increase in electron density on the *ortho* carbon atom. These changes, in turn, increase the electron density on the other *ortho* and *para* carbon atoms.

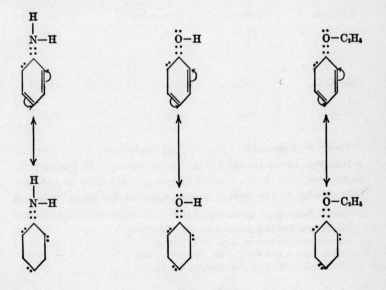

The basic functional groups produce two main effects on the phenyl group: (1) increased electron densities at the *ortho* and *para* positions, and (2) increased electron density of the ring due to electron release toward the ring.

4. Mechanism of Ring Substitution.

A discussion of the effect of acidic and basic functional groups on the benzenoid ring would not be complete without a brief mention of their relationship to the mechanism of substitution on the ring.

Ingold,[1,2] Robinson,[3] and Price[6] have laid the foundation of, and also elaborated on, an electronic interpretation of ring substitutions. The orientating influence of acidic and basic radicals can be adequately explained if it is assumed that the substituent is an acid radical.[7]

The experimental evidence[8,9] indicates that the substitution is probably produced by the action of "positive fragments" on the benzenoid system. These electrophilic (acidic) fragments are either *produced* by catalysts[10] or if *already* present their concentration will be increased by the presence of a catalyst (Table 1).

TABLE 1

REAGENT	CATALYST	POSITIVE FRAGMENT (STRONG ACID)	NEGATIVE FRAGMENT (WEAK BASE)
$CH_3 \colon \ddot{Br} \colon$	$FeBr_3$	CH_3^{+1}	$FeBr_4^{-1}$
$CH_3 - \overset{\colon \ddot{O}}{\underset{\colon \colon}{C}} \colon \ddot{Cl} \colon$	$AlCl_3$	$\left[CH_3 - \overset{\colon \ddot{O}}{C} \right]^{+1}$	$AlCl_4^{-1}$
$\colon \ddot{Cl} \colon \ddot{Cl} \colon$	BCl_3	$\left[\colon \ddot{Cl} \right]^{+1}$	BCl_4^{-1}

These strongly acidic "positive fragments" will attack the benzenoid rings at the points of high electron density. In the previous section we have shown that acidic radicals will increase the electron density at the *meta* positions, whereas the basic functional

[6] Price, *Chem. Revs.*, **29**, 53 (1941).
[7] Luder and Zuffanti, *Chem. Revs.*, **34**, 350 (1944).
[8] Bodendorf and Bohme, *Ann.*, **516**, 1 (1935).
[9] Wertyporoch and Firla, *Ann.*, **500**, 287 (1933).
[10] Ramser and Wiberg, *Ber.*, **63B**, 1136 (1930).

groups will increase the electron density at the *ortho* and *para* positions.

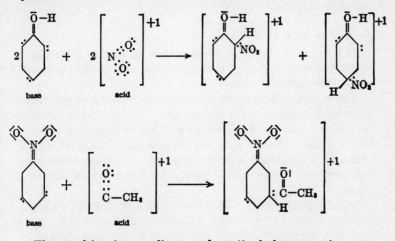

The resulting intermediate products [11] of these reactions are thermodynamically unstable compounds that become stabilized by proton expulsion to return to a resonating benzenoid structure:

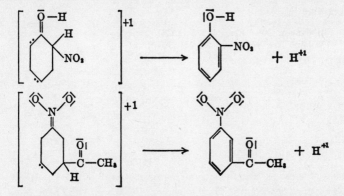

It is to be kept in mind that the benzenoid formula shown for the final compound represents only one of many possible resonance structures. The formula is not presented as being the one and only correct electronic configuration. To represent the mechanism of a further substitution we would have to show the electronic effect produced on the benzenoid ring by the two groups

[11] Pfeiffer and Wizinger, *Ann.*, **461**, 132 (1928).

already present. In this manner we would know the points of high electron density and thus be able to predict the point of attack in the ring.

5. Ease of Ring Substitution.

Holleman [12] has made a careful study of the role played by a large number of acidic and basic radicals in the nitration of benzenoid compounds.

The presence of an acidic radical, on a benzenoid ring, causes an overall decrease in electron density. The result is a decrease in activity in substitution reactions (since the entering group is electrophilic). Organic chemists have long been familiar with the difficulty of nitrating a compound such as nitrobenzene or benzenesulfonic acid. Concentrated nitric acid is required for the nitrations.

Basic radicals, on the other hand, cause an overall increase in electron density on the benzenoid ring. The increase in the number of electrons in the ring would tend to produce increased activity. Thus a substance such as phenol can be nitrated very easily; dilute nitric acid will produce a mixture of *ortho* and *para* nitrophenols. Also toluene can be nitrated fourteen times as fast as benzene. [13]

[12] Holleman, *Chem. Revs.*, **1**, 187 (1925).
[13] Wibaut, *Rec. trav. chim.*, **34**, 241 (1915).

Chapter 6

NEUTRALIZATION

This chapter and those following it are concerned with the four experimental criteria of acids and bases adopted by Lewis: neutralization, titration with indicators, displacement, and catalysis.

Neutralization is the formation of a coordinate covalent bond between a primary acid (see Chapter 3) and a primary base, e.g.,

$$H^{+1} + :\ddot{O}:H^{-1} \rightarrow H:\ddot{O}:H \tag{1}$$

$$\underset{\text{acid}}{Ag^{+1}} + \underset{\text{base}}{2:NH_3} \rightarrow Ag(:NH_3)_2^{+1} \tag{2}$$

It is customary to consider that the "hydrogen ion" occurs as a solvated proton, for example, the hydronium ion in water or the ammonium ion in liquid ammonia:

$$H:\ddot{O}:H^{+1} \qquad H:\ddot{N}:H^{+1}$$
$$\ddot{H} \qquad\qquad \ddot{H}$$

These cations are both secondary acids, and their reactions would involve displacement, not neutralization (Chapter 8). It is customary to disregard solvation of metallic ions such as the acidic silver ion in equation 2. Yet there is no doubt that the silver ion and other acidic ions in water solution are solvated as is the proton. Apparently we may speak either of neutralization or of displacement, depending upon our point of view. This question will be discussed further in Chapter 8.

However, when there seems to be no doubt that a primary acid (e.g., boron trichloride in the absence of a solvent) is involved, there is no difficulty in using the term *neutralization*. At any rate, the electronic theory of acids and bases gives definite meaning to the word. The type equation of the Brønsted theory

$$acid_1 + base_2 \rightarrow acid_2 + base_1 \tag{3}$$

is often assumed to dispose of the concept of neutralization. We shall see in Chapter 8 that this is not the case. The equation may represent the fact that acids or bases will replace weaker acids or bases from their compounds. It does not abolish neutralization.

The acid boron trichloride is neutralized by the base triethylamine when both substances are in the pure liquid or gaseous state:

$$
\overset{\displaystyle \cdot\cdot}{:\!\ddot{C}l\!:} \quad Et \qquad\qquad \overset{\displaystyle \cdot\cdot}{:\!\ddot{C}l\!:} \quad Et
$$
$$
:\!\ddot{C}l\!:\!\ddot{B} + :\!\ddot{N}\!:\!Et \rightarrow :\!\ddot{C}l\!:\!\ddot{B} \ : \ \ddot{N}\!:\!Et \qquad (4)
$$
$$
:\!\ddot{C}l\!: \quad \ddot{E}t \qquad\qquad :\!\ddot{C}l\!: \quad \ddot{E}t
$$

The product is usually called a molecular or addition compound. In some cases it may be a salt. In this particular example the possibility of ionization of one of the chlorine atoms ought to be considered. When the boron chloride gains a share in the lone pair of electrons on the nitrogen atom, the boron atom is made more negative, thus repelling the chlorine electrons. It may not occur to a great extent in this particular compound, but where sufficient electrical "strain" is set up, upon the acceptance of a share in another electron pair by the acid, one would expect ionization to be favored. Such ionization in solution would, of course, be greatly affected by the dielectric constant of the solvent. Three examples of ionization, of the many that could be given, are the following:

$$
C_5H_5N + HCl \rightarrow C_5H_5NH^{+1} + Cl^{-1} \qquad (5)
$$

$$
AlCl_3 + COCl_2 \rightarrow COCl^{+1} + AlCl_4{}^{-1} \qquad (6)
$$

$$
SnCl_4 + 2SeOCl_2 \rightarrow 2SeOCl^{+1} + SnCl_6{}^{-2} \qquad (7)
$$

In these and similar examples the product is usually considered a salt. There seems to be no need for the name "pseudo salt." It would appear that when such compounds are crystallized from the solvent the ions may persist in the solid state. (We use the word *salt* to mean an ionic compound.) Hence, we would call the compounds salts.

However, the formation of a salt is not always the result. According to the water theory of acids and bases, a salt invariably resulted from neutralization; but salt formation is obviously unnecessary, as the following examples show:

$$
\underset{\text{acid}}{SO_3} + \underset{\text{base}}{HOH} \rightarrow H_2SO_4 \qquad (8)
$$

$$
\underset{\text{acid}}{BCl_3} + \underset{\text{base}}{(CH_3)_2O} \rightarrow [(CH_3)_2O \rightarrow BCl_3] \qquad (9)
$$

The essential thing in neutralization is the formation of the coordinate covalent bond.

The neutralization product is not necessarily neutral in the sense that it is no longer either acidic or basic. Unfortunate as this may seem, it is a familiar fact. For example, in equation 8 the neutralization product, sulfuric acid, is still strongly acidic. In equation 9 the product is definitely amphoteric in subsequent displacement reactions with either acids or bases.

Neutralization does not necessarily involve the solvent. Some discussion of the role of the solvent will be given in Chapter 8. Here we shall consider a few reactions which do not involve the solvent. Some have already been mentioned, e.g., the gaseous phase reaction between boron fluoride and amines or ammonia. Others occurring at high temperatures have been listed by Audrieth and Moeller.[1] The formation of certain electrolytic melts, borax and metaphosphate bead tests, the manufacture of glass and cement, and the formation of slag in the blast furnace may all be classified as neutralization reactions.[2]

Some of them might also be classified as acid-base displacement, depending upon how the choice of base is made, as the following examples indicate:

$$FeS + S^{-2} \rightarrow FeS_2{}^{-2} \tag{10}$$

$$AlF_3 + 3F^{-1} \rightarrow AlF_6{}^{-3} \tag{11}$$

$$\underset{\text{acid}}{SiO_2} + \underset{\text{base}}{O^{-2}} \rightarrow SiO_3{}^{-2} \tag{12}$$

Equation 12 might represent displacement rather than neutralization if the oxide ion comes from an oxide which is not ionic. (Note that in equations 11 and 12 the central acidic atom of the product in each reaction has twelve valence electrons—two more violations of the old "rule of eight" discussed in Chapter 2.)

The effect of the solvent upon neutralization will be treated in Chapter 8 since a previous discussion of displacement is necessary. The type equation of the Brønsted theory eliminates neutralization from all acid-base reactions covered by the theory. This is because the equation represents displacement reactions of secondary acids and bases. Since the Lewis theory includes the Brønsted

[1] Audrieth and Moeller, *J. Chem. Education*, **20**, 219 (1943).
[2] An interesting application to glass manufacture is given in a paper by Sun and Silverman, *J. Am. Ceramic Soc.*, **28**, 8 (1945).

theory we reach the same conclusion as far as hydrogen acids are concerned. However, the Lewis theory does give meaning to the term neutralization as applied to reactions between primary acids and bases. Neutralization is the combination of a primary acid with a primary base to form a coordinate covalent bond between the two.

Chapter 7

TITRATIONS WITH INDICATORS

1. Introduction.

The second of the experimental criteria of acids and bases is their behavior in titrations against each other with the aid of indicators. Such titrations may be performed in a great variety of solvents.

Lewis [1] titrated bases like pyridine and triethylamine with acids such as solutions of BCl_3 and $SnCl_4$ in carbon tetrachloride, and $AgClO_4$ dissolved in benzene. These solutions were titrated back and forth with the use of indicators such as thymol blue, butter yellow, and crystal violet. Crystal violet is an especially convenient indicator because of its solubility in a variety of solvents and because it usually gives the same color change in different solvents.

Comparison by means of a series of titrations is one method of establishing whether certain substances are acids or bases. One example of the titration procedures is given in the next section. Titrations of the above solutions make it obvious that there are many acids other than H-acids and many bases other than HO-bases. This fact is not surprising when the fundamental electrophilic and electrodotic characteristics of such substances are considered.

[1] Lewis, *J. Franklin Inst.*, **226**, 293 (1938).

2. Experimental Titrations.

The following experiments [2] demonstrate only a few of the many titrations that can be carried out to show the acidic and basic characteristics of compounds.

WATER USED AS SOLVENT. The indicator used in this series of experiments is crystal violet dissolved in water.

Acids (HCl, H_2SO_4, $HC_2H_3O_2$, HNO_3). Ten milliliters of water is poured into each of four 6-inch test tubes, and 3 or 4 drops of the indicator is added. The violet color that results can be changed to yellow by the addition of acid. When dilute acid is added slowly, the intermediate green color may easily be observed. The HCl, H_2SO_4, $HC_2H_3O_2$, and HNO_3 are used, one in each tube, to show this color change.

The reaction is explained by the fact that these acid solutions contain the hydronium ion, H_3O^{+1}, which is electrophilic.

Bases (NH_3, C_5H_5N, C_2H_5OH, 1,4-dioxane). The basic characteristics of these compounds can be demonstrated by the addition of a few drops of each to the four yellow solutions obtained in the above experiment. In each solution the color is changed back from yellow to violet on the addition of the base. These compounds are bases because they are electron-pair donors and can form coordinate covalent bonds with the protons of the above-mentioned acids.

Example:

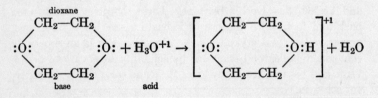

CHLOROBENZENE USED AS SOLVENT. The indicator used in these experiments is crystal violet dissolved in chlorobenzene.

Acids (HCl (gas) dissolved in C_6H_5Cl, BCl_3 dissolved in C_6H_5Cl, and fuming $SnCl_4$). Ten milliliters of chlorobenzene is poured into each of three 6-inch test tubes, and 3 or 4 drops of the indicator is added to each tube. The violet color that results can be changed to yellow by the addition of a few drops of an acid. The above acids are used to show this color change, one in each test

[2] Luder, McGuire, and Zuffanti, *J. Chem. Education*, **20**, 344 (1943).

tube. Here again we have substances that are acidic because they are electron-pair acceptors.

Bases (ethers, carboxylic acid anhydrides, alcohols).

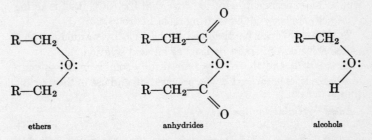

ethers   anhydrides   alcohols

All these substances can be demonstrated to be bases by allowing them to react with the acids mentioned above. If these bases are added to the yellow solutions formed in the first part of this experiment, the violet color of the indicator quickly reappears.

Example:

phthalic acid anhydride

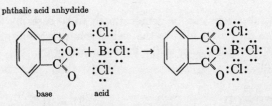

base   acid

CARBON TETRACHLORIDE USED AS SOLVENT. The indicator used is crystal violet dissolved in chlorobenzene rather than in carbon tetrachloride. (The indicator is quite insoluble in carbon tetrachloride, but when it is added in chlorobenzene solution no precipitation takes place; a clear solution results.)

Acids (BCl_3, HCl (gas) dissolved in CCl_4, and $AlCl_3$ in CCl_4). Ten milliliters of anhydrous carbon tetrachloride is poured into each of three 6-inch test tubes and 3 or 4 drops of the indicator is added to each tube. The violet color that results can be changed to yellow by the addition of some of these acids.

The $AlCl_3$ is not very soluble in CCl_4. Shaking the mixture for a considerable length of time and then filtering gives a clear filtrate which does not behave as an acid. If any hydrolysis should take place, due to the presence of traces of moisture, the resulting HCl gas would dissolve in the solvent and an acid reaction would be observed.

If some of the original mixture of $AlCl_3$ suspended in CCl_4 is used, however, the violet color of the indicator disappears and the resulting yellow color shows that the solid $AlCl_3$ is behaving as an acid. This experiment helps to prove that the $AlCl_3$ itself is acting as an acid, not any HCl resulting from hydrolysis.

Enough $AlCl_3$ can be dissolved in the CCl_4 by warming so that a clear solution of it may be used as an acid solution.

As the BCl_3 and the HCl gas are readily soluble in the solvent, no trouble is encountered in the preparation and use of these acidic solutions.

Bases (pyridine, amines, esters).

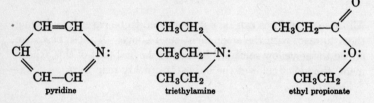

pyridine   triethylamine   ethyl propionate

These substances can be demonstrated to be bases by the fact that when they are added to the yellow solutions resulting in the first part, the violet color of the indicator reappears.

Example:

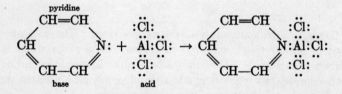

base   acid

Discussion. In all these experiments the acidic substances are those that contain atoms capable of accepting a share in an electron pair and the bases are those substances containing atoms capable of donating a share in an electron pair.

It is obvious that hydrogen chloride behaves as an acid regardless of whether it is dissolved in water, chlorobenzene, carbon tetrachloride, or any other solvent. (In water solutions of the common acids it is the H^{+1} or H_3O^{+1} that behaves as an acid, whereas in the organic solvents it is the molecules of the compounds that behave as acids.) The same may be said for all other compounds that are capable of accepting electron pairs.

It is also clear that compounds like pyridine, alcohols, ethers, and many other substances act as bases whether dissolved in water, chloroform, carbon tetrachloride, chlorobenzene, or any other solvent that will dissolve them, because fundamentally these bases are compounds that are capable of donating an electron pair.

3. Indicator Color Changes.

The observation that different acids cause the same color change is readily explained as follows.

The addition of increasing amounts of an acid to a solution of crystal violet will cause the violet color to change to green and then to yellow. Rosenstein and Adams [3] explained these changes in water solution as due to the successive addition of H^{+1} to the dimethylamino groups of the indicator.

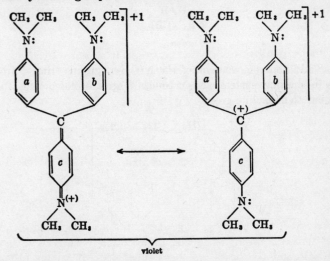

The above formulas represent two of the several possible resonance structures that can be written to show the violet form of the indicator. It is obvious that the unshared electron pair on the nitrogen atom of each $N(CH_3)_2$ group can form a quinoid structure as shown in ring c of the left-hand formula. Other resonance structures would have ring a or b as the quinoid ring.[4] If H^{+1} or

[3] Rosenstein and Adams, *J. Am. Chem. Soc.*, **36**, 1452 (1914).

[4] Wheland, *The Theory of Resonance*, John Wiley & Sons, New York, 1944, pp. 153 and 185.

BF$_3$ or any other electrophilic substance is added to the indicator solution, coordination with one of the unshared pairs of electrons will result.

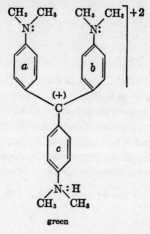

green

This addition removes one of the N(CH$_3$)$_2$ groups (ring *c*) from the resonating system and produces a green-colored substance similar to malachite green.

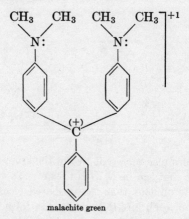

malachite green

Further color change to yellow is produced by the addition of a second H^{+1} to another N(CH$_3$)$_2$ group, leaving only one N(CH$_3$)$_2$ group in the resonating system.[5]

[5] Conant and Werner, *J. Am. Chem. Soc.*, **52,** 4436 (1930).

Clearly, the presence of any strongly electrophilic substance such as BCl_3, $AlCl_3$, $AgClO_4$, SO_3, and $SnCl_4$ could result in co-ordination in a similar manner to the behavior of the H-acids. The color changes are the same regardless of the acid or solvent used. Lewis and Bigeleisen[6] give a quantitative demonstration that H^{+1} or $SnCl_4$ added to one $-NR_2$ of methylene blue results in almost identical spectra.

The addition of basic (electrodotic) substances would, of course, neutralize any of the above acids in the solution and also remove from the dye molecule the coordinated electrophiles. This reaction would again return the $N(CH_3)_2$ groups to the resonating system of the dye molecule, and the green and then the violet colors would reappear.

Thus the electronic theory provides a simple and consistent explanation of the experimental behavior of a great variety of acids and bases toward indicators.

[6] Lewis and Bigeleisen, *J. Am. Chem. Soc.*, **65**, 1147 (1943).

Chapter 8

DISPLACEMENT

1. Introduction.

The third experimental criterion of acids and bases is displacement. There are two types of acid-base displacement: (1) a strong acid in general will displace a weaker one from combination with a base; (2) a strong base will displace a weaker one from combination with an acid. A weaker coordinate bond is broken to form a stronger one.

A familiar example of the first type of displacement (of a weaker acid by a stronger one) is the liberation of carbon dioxide from sodium carbonate solution upon the addition of hydrogen chloride:

$$\underset{\text{acid}}{2H^{+1}} + CO_3^{-2} \rightarrow H_2O + \underset{\text{acid}}{CO_2} \tag{1}$$

The hydrogen ions displace the weak acid, carbon dioxide, from combination with the oxide ion. Another example described by G. N. Lewis [1] is the displacement of carbon dioxide when finely divided sodium carbonate is warmed with boron trichloride or stannic chloride in a mixture of carbon tetrachloride and acetone. The other product was not analyzed, but the reaction might be written tentatively as:

$$\underset{\text{acid}}{BCl_3} + Na_2CO_3 \rightarrow [Na_2O{\rightarrow}BCl_3] + \underset{\text{acid}}{CO_2} \tag{2}$$

Another example of the displacement of one acid by another is the high-temperature reaction (favored by the volatility of the CO_2):

$$\underset{\text{acid}}{SiO_2} + Na_2CO_3 \rightarrow Na_2SiO_3 + \underset{\text{acid}}{CO_2} \tag{3}$$

[1] Lewis, *J. Franklin Inst.*, **226**, 304 (1938).

Examples of the second kind of displacement (of a weak base by a stronger one) are more familiar, since the type equation of the Brønsted theory represents the displacement of one base by a stronger base in competition for the proton, for example:

$$H_2O + HCl \rightarrow H_3O^{+1} + Cl^{-1} \qquad (4)$$
base   base

Water acting as a base displaces the weaker base, chloride ion, from combination with the proton. Another example that does not involve the proton is the displacement of ammonia from combination with trimethylboron by trimethylamine: [2]

$$(CH_3)_3N: + H_3N:B(CH_3)_3 \rightarrow (CH_3)_3N:B(CH_3)_3 + :NH_3$$
base   base

2. Hydrogen Acids.

Some writers have indicated that hydrogen acids require special consideration in the Lewis terminology. No doubt such a misunderstanding arises from the emphasis of the Brønsted theory upon displacement of one base by another as the only criterion of acid-base phenomena. Actually displacement is only one of the four "phenomenological criteria" of acids and bases, and the Brønsted type equation is only one of the two types of acid-base displacement. The Brønsted theory is thus included in the Lewis theory and requires no special consideration.

In order to show that special treatment is unnecessary for hydrogen acids, we need only demonstrate that the displacement reaction represented by the typical Brønsted equation is not unique. The same kind of reaction may take place between many other acids and bases. A detailed consideration of one example should be sufficient illustration. When the addition compound formed by the neutralization of boron trichloride by acetone is added to pyridine, displacement of the weaker base (acetone) by the stronger base (pyridine) takes place.[1] This reaction is exactly analogous to the displacement of the weakly basic chloride ion from combination with the proton when hydrogen chloride is added to water:

[2] Brown, *J. Am. Chem. Soc.*, **67**, 378 (1945).

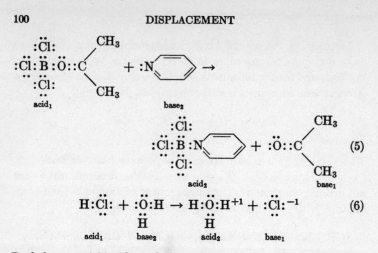

$$H:\ddot{Cl}: + :\ddot{O}:H \rightarrow H:\ddot{O}:H^{+1} + :\ddot{Cl}:^{-1} \qquad (6)$$
$$\overset{\cdot\cdot}{H} \qquad\qquad \overset{\cdot\cdot}{H}$$

acid₁   base₂   acid₂   base₁

Both boron trichloride and the proton are primary acids which, to form the $acid_1$ compounds shown above, have been neutralized by the weak bases acetone and chloride ion, respectively. However, in both the resulting compounds, stronger bases are able to displace the weaker ones from combination with the two acids. All four acids (in both equations) are secondary acids.

Many more examples of displacement reactions of exactly the same type could be given. Some of them are responsible for catalysis and will be considered in the following chapters. One familiar example is interesting since it has been the subject of some misunderstanding:

$$Ag(NH_3)_2{}^{+1} + OH^{-1} \rightleftarrows AgOH + 2NH_3 \qquad (7)$$

acid₁   base₂   acid₂   base₁

The silver ion is a fairly strong acid which will combine with many bases, including ammonia and hydroxide ion. The reaction represented by the above equation is analogous to any Brønsted type equation, for example:

$$NH_4{}^{+1} + OH^{-1} \rightleftarrows HOH + NH_3 \qquad (8)$$

acid₁   base₂   acid₂   base₁

A number of statements appear in the literature to the effect that, "in dilute aqueous solution, silver ions do not combine with hydroxyl ions . . . whereas they do combine with ammonia." [3] The solubility product for silver hydroxide and the instability constant for the ammonia complex, however, are respectively 2×10^{-8} and

³ Kolthoff, *J. Phys. Chem.*, **48**, 51 (1944).

6×10^{-8}. Silver ions and ammonia molecules combine until equilibrium is reached when their concentrations are low. Silver ions and hydroxide ions *also* combine until equilibrium is reached when the concentrations of both ions are low. If the two ions have been added in equal amounts, equilibrium is attained when each has a concentration equal to 1.4×10^{-4} M. Now if in the other solution the concentrations of ammonia and silver ion in equilibrium with the complex ion are adjusted to have comparable molarities, that is, 1.4×10^{-4} M, the concentration of the complex is 0.47×10^{-4} M. In such a solution only about one-fourth of the silver ions have combined to form the complex. Thus under comparable conditions a large proportion of the silver ions do not combine with ammonia molecules.

Perhaps the cause of the misunderstanding lies in the method by which we are accustomed to observe the preparation of the silver-ammonia complex. When we add excess ammonia solution to silver nitrate solution the initial precipitate dissolves, forming the complex ion. This apparently means that ammonia is a much stronger base toward silver ion than hydroxide ion is. But we must remember that the silver hydroxide precipitate is formed first. When the first few drops of ammonia solution are added the ammonia is so dilute that it is largely ionized to form hydroxide ions which coordinate[4] with the silver ions to form the hydroxide. But, by the time the precipitate is completely dissolved, the amount of ammonia added is enough so that if the silver ion were not present the concentration of NH_3 would be roughly 100 times the concentration of OH^{-1} ion. Actually, if concentrated sodium hydroxide solution is now added to the solution, the ammonia is displaced and the precipitate returns. This is what one would expect when mass-action effects are taken into account. The effects observed are similar whether the acid is the proton or the silver ion. The displacement of one base by another depends not only upon their relative strengths, but upon concentration factors also.

[4] Since silver hydroxide actually appears as silver oxide when attempts are made to isolate it, we cannot be positive that a coordinate bond is formed between silver and hydroxide ions. However, there are two reasons for believing that one is formed: (1) other hydroxides of similar nature (small positive ion) are often not ionic even in the solid state; (2) silver iodide does not crystallize into an ionic lattic although the chloride and bromide do.

An idea of the relative basic strengths of ammonia and hydroxide ions toward silver ion can be obtained from equation 7. The equilibrium constant for equation 7 is

$$K = \frac{[NH_3]^2}{[Ag(NH_3)_2{}^{+1}] \times [OH^{-1}]} \qquad (9)$$

which may be evaluated by combining

$$\frac{[Ag^{+1}] \times [NH_3]^2}{[Ag(NH_3)_2{}^{+1}]} = 6 \times 10^{-8} \qquad (10)$$

with

$$[Ag^{+1}] \times [OH^{-1}] = 2 \times 10^{-8} \qquad (11)$$

We see that the constant has a value of 3, indicating that ammonia is about as strong a base as hydroxyl ion toward silver ion.

It is worth while noting at this point that in equations 5, 7, and 8 the acid$_1$ and acid$_2$ compounds are amphoteric in exactly the same sense. The addition compounds of boron trichloride with acetone and with pyridine are amphoteric because they contain both acidic and basic constituents. They can react both ways because stronger bases will displace the weaker bases and stronger acids will displace the boron trichloride. In the same way silver hydroxide in equation 7 and water in equation 8 are also amphoteric. They appear as acids in these equations, but both may act as bases because of the presence of the hydroxyl group.

3. Neutralization and the Solvent.

When the solvent takes part in acid-base phenomena, the reactions are usually displacement reactions. Considering only acid-base reactions, solvents may be divided into three classes: (1) those that are ordinarily inert toward acids and bases, e.g., benzene, carbon tetrachloride, and chlorobenzene; (2) those that are ionizable, e.g., water, ammonia, sulfur dioxide, phosgene, and selenium oxychloride; (3) those that do not ionize but do react with acids and bases, e.g., ether and pyridine. If we consider the neutralization of boron trichloride by triethylamine in the three types of solvents, we find that the net result may be the same as when the neutralization occurs in the absence of a solvent:

$$(C_2H_5)_3N: + BCl_3 \rightarrow (C_2H_5)_3N:BCl_3 \quad \text{(neutralization)} \quad (12)$$

When the solvent is inert it is merely a diluent and the neutralization product is obtained directly. When the solvent is ionizable, intermediate displacement reactions with the solvent may be observed. If either the acid or the base, or both, are strong enough, they will at least partially displace cations or anions of the solvent; e.g., if selenium oxychloride is chosen as the solvent:

$$BCl_3 + SeOCl_2 \rightarrow SeOCl^{+1} + BCl_4{}^{-1} \quad \text{(displacement)} \quad (13)$$

$$(C_2H_5)_3N: + SeOCl_2 \rightarrow$$
$$(C_2H_5)_3N:SeOCl^{+1} + Cl^{-1} \quad \text{(displacement)} \quad (14)$$

When the two solutions are mixed, the following reaction takes place:

$$SeOCl^{+1}, BCl_4{}^{-1} + (C_2H_5)_3N:SeOCl^{+1}, Cl^{-1} \rightarrow$$
$$(C_2H_5)_3N:BCl_3 + 2SeOCl_2 \quad (15)$$

The same neutralization product is obtained as when the reaction is carried out directly or in an inert solvent.

When the solvent reacts without ionizing, it reacts with either the acid or the base, but not ordinarily with both. Such solvents are usually not amphoteric. For example, if boron trichloride reacts with triethylamine in ether, the boron trichloride would react with the ether, but the triethylamine would not. The oxygen atom in the ether can donate an electron pair to form a coordinate bond, but the hydrogen atoms in ether have little tendency to form hydrogen bridges:

$$(C_2H_5)_2O + BCl_3 \rightarrow [(C_2H_5)_2O \rightarrow BCl_3] \quad (16)$$

When triethylamine is added, it merely displaces the weaker base and the resulting product is the same as before:

$$[(C_2H_5)_2O \rightarrow BCl_3] + (C_2H_5)_3N \rightarrow$$
$$[(C_2H_5)_3N \rightarrow BCl_3] + (C_2H_5)_2O \quad (17)$$

In all four cases the final neutralization product is the same.

These examples help to clarify the relationship of neutralization to displacement mentioned at the beginning of Chapter 6. Neutralization is the formation of the coordinate covalent bond between a primary acid and a primary base. The reaction represented by equation 12 is neutralization, but we note that when a solvent is involved the same result may be obtained through a series of displacements. Equations 13 and 14 are both displacement reactions. Equation 15 represents two simultaneous dis-

placements. At the same time equation 15 also represents neutralization as far as the original primary acid and primary base are
concerned. Whether or not a solvent is used as a medium for this
reaction, the final product is the result of neutralization—the
formation of the coordinate covalent bond between the boron
chloride and triethylamine.

4. The Leveling Effect.

In comparing the relative strengths of acids and bases in a particular solvent such as water, liquid ammonia, or glacial acetic
acid, the range of comparison is limited by the strength of the
solvent as an acid or base.

For example, the difference between perchloric, hydrobromic,
sulfuric, hydrochloric, and nitric acids is obscured in water because
they all react completely with the solvent in dilute solution. The
reaction

$$HCl + H_2O \rightarrow H_3O^{+1} + Cl^{-1}$$

proceeds completely to the right because the water molecule is so
much stronger as a base than chloride ion that it displaces it completely from combination with the proton. The perchlorate,
bromide, bisulfate, and nitrate ions are all similar to the chloride
ion in acting as extremely weak bases.

Since such acids react completely with water, only one acid, the
hydronium ion, is left in solution. Consequently the acids all
appear equally strong. This is known as the *leveling effect*.

A solvent which is more basic than water, e.g., liquid ammonia,
will level the strength of a larger group of acids. For example,
in water, acetic acid is much less ionized than hydrochloric acid
because the acetate ion formed by the reaction

$$HC_2H_3O_2 + H_2O \rightleftarrows H_3O^{+1} + C_2H_3O_2^{-1}$$

is a much stronger base than the chloride ion. Water is not able
to displace it to a very great extent from its combination with
the proton. But when acetic acid is added to liquid ammonia
as a solvent the reaction

$$HC_2H_3O_2 + NH_3 \rightarrow NH_4^{+1} + C_2H_3O_2^{-1}$$

goes all the way to completion.[5] Ammonia is a stronger base than
water and is so much stronger than the acetate ion that it

[5] Schwarzenbach, *Helv. Chim. Acta*, **13**, 870 (1930).

is able to displace it completely. Thus in liquid ammonia all acids stronger than acetic acid will appear to have the same strength, that of the ammonium ion. Since the ammonium ion is weaker than the hydronium ion, we say that the strength of acids is leveled *down* farther in ammonia than in water.

Obviously a solvent more acidic than water would have a similar leveling effect on bases such as ammonia and the amines.

The leveling effect is one phenomenon that must be taken into account when comparing relative acid or base strengths. Since water levels downward the strengths of the strong acids like hydrogen chloride, it is necessary to use a less basic solvent such as acetic acid or even an "inactive" one like benzene. In acetic acid the reaction

$$HCl + HC_2H_3O_2 \rightleftarrows H_2C_2H_3O_2{}^{+1} + Cl^{-1}$$

has little tendency to proceed to the right because acetic acid is so weakly basic. Hence a comparison with other acids is possible. It has been found that $HClO_4 > HBr > H_2SO_4 > HCl > HNO_3$ gives the relative strengths of these strong acids in acetic acid as a solvent.[6]

5. The Strengths of Acids and Bases.

In the preceding section we have tacitly assumed that the familiar method of comparing the strengths of acids and bases by displacement reactions yields values which are independent of the reference base or acid. This is not the case, as several investigators including Lewis have shown. However, the exceptions are usually obvious and as yet probably do not warrant discarding the idea of monotonic series for the confusion that would thereupon result. To quote Lewis: "The fact that we can thus get a satisfactory acidity function over the whole range from pure water to pure sulfur trioxide shows the desirability of attempting to construct a monotonic series of acids even though we have pointed out that it can never be exact and that there may be some very large specific variations." [7]

One of the exceptions referred to by Lewis occurs in the reversal of the relative strengths of triethylamine and ammonia. Ammonia is the weaker base toward the proton, but, when the reference acid is *m*-dinitrobenzene, ammonia appears to be much stronger than

[6] Conant and Hall, *J. Am. Chem. Soc.*, **49**, 3062 (1927).

[7] Lewis and Bigeleisen, *J. Am. Chem. Soc.*, **65**, 1144 (1943).

triethylamine. Double chelation is the explanation advanced by Lewis and Seaborg.[8]

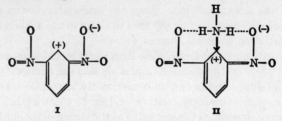

Formula I represents one of the resonating structures of *m*-dinitrobenzene. Formula II represents the compound formed upon the addition of ammonia. Obviously such double chelation is not to be expected from triethylamine.

Another interesting example of reversal from the expected order of basic strength is given by H. C. Brown.[2] Using displacement reactions of the type

$$(CH_3)_3N: + H_3N:B(CH_3)_3 \rightleftarrows (CH_3)_3N:B(CH_3)_3 + :NH_3$$

he found, for example, that, when trimethylboron is used as the reference acid, trimethylamine is a stronger base than ammonia, as it is toward the proton. (Note that the above reaction is a displacement reaction entirely analogous to the type equation of the Brønsted theory.) But when the reference acid is changed to tri-*t*-butylboron, the order is reversed. The explanation advanced is given in terms of "F-strain." "F-strain is that strain which is caused by steric interference of the atoms or groups which are attached to different atoms resulting in a force which tends to separate the two atoms."[2]

[8] Lewis and Seaborg, *J. Am. Chem. Soc.*, **62**, 2122 (1940).

Chapter 9

CATALYSIS

1. Nature of Catalysis.

The fourth criterion of acid and base behavior suggested by G. N. Lewis is *catalysis*. The following chapters represent an attempt to discuss this criterion systematically. Familiar examples of acid-base catalysis are considered from the Lewis viewpoint in order to show that there is no essential difference in catalytic behavior whether protons are involved or not.

"Catalysis" as usually defined has implied that the catalyst is recovered unchanged. There seems to be a tendency to broaden the definition. For example, Hammett [1] points out that there is no important distinction between catalysis in the older sense and the kind of acceleration produced by a base which appears as its "conjugate acid" at the end of the reaction. A few of the examples presented here are of the conjugate type, but most of them conform to the older definition.

Since it is already generally recognized that basic behavior is displayed by a very large number of substances,[2-8] only enough examples of base-catalyzed reactions are included here to show that when a base acts as a catalyst the substance attacked by the base is behaving as an acid.

[1] Hammett, *Physical Organic Chemistry*, McGraw-Hill Book Company, New York, 1940, p. 230.

[2] Branch and Calvin, *Theory of Organic Chemistry*, Prentice-Hall, New York, 1941, p. 414.

[3] Brønsted, *Rec. trav. chim.*, **42**, 718 (1923).

[4] Lowry, *Chemistry & Industry*, **42**, 43 (1923).

[5] Kalnin, *Helv. Chim. Acta*, **11**, 977 (1928).

[6] Adams, *Organic Reactions*, John Wiley & Sons, New York, Vol. I, pp. 267 and 276.

[7] Hauser and Renfrow, *J. Am. Chem. Soc.*, **59**, 1823 (1937).

[8] Hudson and Hauser, *J. Am. Chem. Soc.*, **63**, 3156 (1941).

However, in spite of the fact that numerous examples of typically acidic properties displayed by substances which do not contain protons have already been listed by many writers,[9, 10] the idea that acidic behavior does not depend upon protons and, in fact, is as widespread as basic behavior is not yet widely accepted. So in our discussion of catalysis, the principal emphasis is upon systematic application of the new theory to acidic catalysis rather than to basic catalysis.

2. Acid Catalysis.

Evidence has been cited previously to show that the common Friedel-Crafts type catalysts such as aluminum chloride, ferric chloride, stannic chloride, and zinc chloride are acids. Their catalytic activity is well known in connection with organic reactions, but it is not usually recognized that they also catalyze such common reactions as those of metals with water. The reaction of iron with pure water to give hydrogen is a very slow one because the concentration of hydrogen ions is so low. Any acid sufficiently strong to increase the hydrogen-ion concentration substantially will accelerate the reaction. It is immaterial whether the acid is *molecular* hydrogen chloride, acetic acid, sulfur trioxide, carbon dioxide, stannic chloride, or *ionic* zinc chloride or cupric sulfate. The rate of reaction depends upon increasing the hydrogen-ion concentration, which in turn depends upon the concentration and strength of the acid which is displacing protons from the water. We shall see that this *increase in positive-ion concentration is typical of acid catalysis.* Obviously these ideas may have a far-reaching effect on the study of corrosion. Corrosion of metals is a complex subject, but it would seem that application of the electronic theory of acids and bases might be helpful in its investigation.

Since the Friedel-Crafts catalysts are usually thought of as halides of a few metals, a natural question to raise might be: If these halides are really acids differing in no fundamental manner from H-acids in their behavior, why do not H-acids catalyze reactions of the Friedel-Crafts type also? The answer is that they do. Hydrogen fluoride,[11] phosphoric acid, and sulfuric acid [12, 13] have

[9] Lewis, *J. Franklin Inst.*, **226**, 293 (1938).

[10] Luder, *Chem. Revs.* **27**, 547 (1940). See Chapter 10 for additional references.

[11] Simons and Archer, *J. Am. Chem. Soc.*, **60**, 2953 (1938).

[12] Burwell and Archer, *J. Am. Chem. Soc.*, **64**, 1032 (1942).

[13] Ipatieff, Corson, and Pines, *J. Am. Chem. Soc.*, **58**, 2339 (1936).

been established as catalysts for Friedel-Crafts and similar reactions.

The catalytic activity of sulfuric acid seems especially interesting. Depending on the concentration of water or of sulfur trioxide, either sulfur trioxide or the H-acid or both may be responsible for the catalysis. Lewis and Bigeleisen [14] have shown [15] that the very rapid increase in the acidity function of Hammett and Deyrup as 100 per cent sulfuric acid is approached is probably due to sulfur trioxide. This might indicate that in the sulfonation of benzene the sulfur trioxide is the principal agent in a direct electrophilic attack.

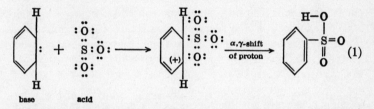

base   acid   (1)

Bordwell, Suter, and Webber [16] have found this concept [17] useful in explaining the mechanism for the reaction of dioxane sulfotrioxide with olefins.

The Friedel-Crafts reactions are *acid-catalyzed* and can be taken as typical examples of this type of catalysis. For example, the alkylation of benzene by an alcohol may be represented as follows:

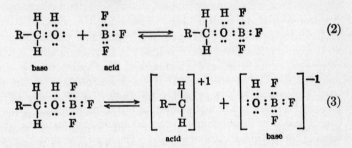

(2)

(3)

[14] The similarity of the absorption curves for methylene blue in stannic chloride and in sulfuric acid, given by the same authors, is a striking demonstration of the essential likeness in the behavior of these two acids toward indicators.

[15] Lewis and Bigeleisen, *J. Am. Chem. Soc.*, **65**, 1144 (1943).

[16] Bordwell, Suter, and Webber, *J. Am. Chem. Soc.*, **67**, 829 (1945).

[17] Luder and Zuffanti, *Chem. Revs.*, **34**, 345 (1944).

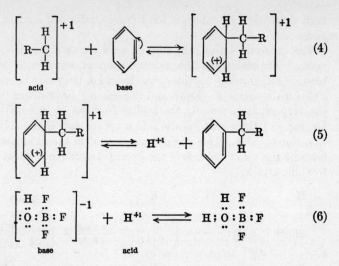

The first step involves the typically acidic behavior of boron trifluoride in accepting a share in a pair of electrons from the alcohol-oxygen[18, 19] to form a coordinate bond. Alcohol is then behaving as a base just as it does according to the Brønsted theory when hydrogen chloride is added to it. The ionization that occurs produces a "positive fragment"[20] which is itself acidic because it has a great tendency to accept a share in an electron pair. Formation of this acid is exactly analogous to any acid-base displacement in which one acid displaces another from combination with a base. The catalytic effect of boron trifluoride in producing this positive fragment is also analogous to the catalytic effect of similar acids in increasing the positive fragment concentration in water, i.e., the hydrogen-ion concentration. As pointed out above, the acceleration of the reaction between iron and water by hydrogen chloride, sulfur trioxide, aluminum chloride, zinc chloride, etc., depends upon the increase in the concentration of hydrogen ions or positive fragments in the water. This formation of positive fragments seems to be typical of acid catalysis. The acid catalyst increases the speed of the reaction by increasing, by displacement, the concentration of the acid group involved in the reaction.

The use of hydrogen fluoride as an acid catalyst in the alkylation

[18] Meerwein and Pannwitz, *J. prakt. Chem.*, **141**, 123 (1934).
[19] O'Leary and Wenzke, *J. Am. Chem. Soc.*, **55**, 2117 (1933).
[20] Price, *Chem. Revs.*, **29**, 37 (1941).

of benzene and phenol with alcohols has also been reported.[21, 22, 23] This reaction again demonstrates the similarity between boron trifluoride and H-acids. It is interesting to note that hydrogen fluoride does not effect *methylations*, although aluminum chloride does.[23] This fact seems to indicate that aluminum chloride is a stronger acid than hydrogen fluoride.

The use of an acid catalyst does not always result in a displacement reaction and the formation of a positive fragment. For example, olefins will react with an acid catalyst [24, 25] in such a manner that a "positive center" is created as shown in the following equation:

$$
\underset{\text{base}}{R{-}\overset{H}{\underset{|}{C}}{::}CH_2} + \underset{\text{acid}}{BF_3} \rightleftarrows R{-}\overset{H}{\underset{(+)}{\underset{|}{C}}}{:}\overset{BF_3}{\ddot{C}H_2} \qquad (7)
$$

The addition compound formed can thus behave in a manner similar to that of the "positive fragments." Obviously, both the carbonium ion (equation 3) and the molecule of the addition compound (equation 7) are electrophilic (acidic) and can force benzene to behave as an electrodote (base).

3. Base Catalysis.

In all the examples of basic catalysis considered in these chapters, the characteristic effect of the basic catalyst is the increase in concentration of the basic group involved in the reaction. In most reactions this is accomplished by the familiar displacement of one base by another, for example, the displacement of the ester anion [7, 26, 27] from an ester:

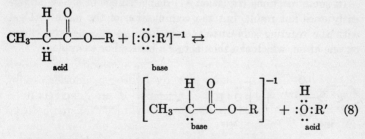

$$
\underset{\text{acid}}{CH_3{-}\overset{H}{\underset{\ddot{H}}{\underset{|}{C}}}{-}\overset{O}{\overset{\|}{C}}{-}O{-}R} + \underset{\text{base}}{[:\ddot{O}:R']^{-1}} \rightleftarrows
$$

$$
\left[\underset{\text{base}}{CH_3{-}\overset{H}{\underset{\ddot{}}{\underset{|}{C}}}{-}\overset{O}{\overset{\|}{C}}{-}O{-}R} \right]^{-1} + \underset{\text{acid}}{\overset{H}{\overset{\ddot{}}{:\ddot{O}:R'}}} \qquad (8)
$$

[21] Simons and Archer, *J. Am. Chem. Soc.*, **62**, 1623 (1940).
[22] Simons, Archer, and Passino, *J. Am. Chem. Soc.*, **60**, 2956 (1938).
[23] Simons and Passino, *J. Am. Chem. Soc.*, **62**, 1624 (1940).
[24] Hunter and Yohe, *J. Am. Chem. Soc.*, **55**, 1248 (1933).
[25] Price and Ciskowski, *J. Am. Chem. Soc.*, **60**, 2499 (1938).
[26] Hauser, *J. Am. Chem. Soc.*, **60**, 1957 (1938).
[27] Arndt and Eistert, *Ber.*, **69**, 2384 (1936).

The increase in the concentration of the ester anion [28], [29] accounts for the increase in reaction rate of the base-catalyzed condensation of the ester,

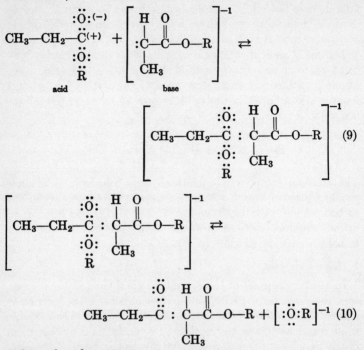

$$(9)$$

$$(10)$$

to form the β-keto ester.

In some reactions (equation 11) displacement of a base apparently does not result, but the combination of the basic catalyst with the reacting substance merely localizes the electron excess on one atom, which can then act as a base. For example:

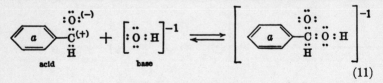

$$(11)$$

In the above reaction, the basic catalyst (OH^{-1}) coordinates with the carbonyl carbon and causes a shift of the C—H electron

[28] Schlenk, Hillemann, and Rodloff, *Ann.*, **487**, 135 (1931).
[29] Muller, Gawlick, and Kreutzmann, *Ann.*, **515**, 97 (1934).

pair,[30] producing $\overset{(+)}{C}—\overset{(-)}{H}$. The product of this reaction can behave as a base because it can furnish a hydride ion [31] to an acid:

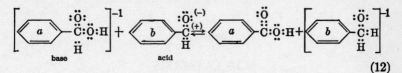

(12)

The examples of basic substances used as catalysts in these and the following illustrations do not differ fundamentally from those considered in illustrations of the Brønsted concept of a base. Admittedly, these substances are proton acceptors, but they can and do react with acid substances other than protons. The proton is only one of many acid groups or compounds having similar electrophilic characteristics. Brønsted's bases are proton acceptors because they can furnish lone pairs of electrons to form a coordinate bond with an acid whether the acid is a proton, a hydronium ion, a neutral H-acid, or any other electron-pair acceptor.

[30] Branch and Calvin, *Theory of Organic Chemistry*, Prentice-Hall, 1941, p. 466.

[31] Hammett, *Physical Organic Chemistry*, McGraw-Hill Book Company, New York, 1940, p. 351.

Chapter 10

ACID CATALYSIS

1. Introduction.

In this chapter it will be assumed that acid catalysis is due to the increased concentration of the acidic group involved in the reaction, caused by the addition of the acid catalyst.

In the preceding chapters it has been shown that the behavior of substances like sulfur trioxide, boron trifluoride, aluminum chloride, stannic chloride, and silver perchlorate is analogous to the behavior of H-acids in neutralization, in displacement, and in titrations with indicators. Many acid-catalyzed reactions will be discussed here in order to emphasize the fact that acidity depends on the electrophilic nature of the reagent and not on the presence of any particular element.

The mechanisms of Friedel-Crafts reactions have been studied extensively. The alkylations involve the use of olefins, alkyl halides, alcohols, ethers, and esters.[1] The acylations make use of acids, esters, acid halides, and acid anhydrides. This type of reaction is *acid-catalyzed*, using such compounds as boron, aluminum, iron, tin, and other metallic halides, as well as sulfuric acid, phosphorus pentoxide, orthophosphoric acid, and hydrogen fluoride. These act as acids in the catalytic activity described because they all have a strong tendency to accept a share in an electron pair as the first step in the reaction.

2. Alkylations.

ALKYL HALIDES. Conductance [2, 3] and dielectric-constant measurements [4] indicate the formation of ionic complexes between the catalyst and the alkyl halide:

$$
\text{R}\overset{\cdot\cdot}{\underset{\cdot\cdot}{\text{X}}}\text{:} + \overset{\cdot\cdot}{\underset{\cdot\cdot}{\text{Al}}}\overset{\overset{\cdot\cdot}{\text{Cl}}\text{:}}{\underset{\underset{\cdot\cdot}{\text{Cl}}\text{:}}{\text{:}}}\overset{\cdot\cdot}{\underset{\cdot\cdot}{\text{Cl}}}\text{:} \rightleftarrows \text{R}\overset{\cdot\cdot}{\underset{\cdot\cdot}{\text{X}}}\text{:}\overset{\cdot\cdot}{\underset{\cdot\cdot}{\text{Al}}}\overset{\overset{\cdot\cdot}{\text{Cl}}\text{:}}{\underset{\underset{\cdot\cdot}{\text{Cl}}\text{:}}{\text{:}}}\overset{\cdot\cdot}{\underset{\cdot\cdot}{\text{Cl}}}\text{:} \rightleftarrows [\text{R}]^{+1} + \left[\overset{\cdot\cdot}{\underset{\cdot\cdot}{\text{X}}}\text{:}\overset{\cdot\cdot}{\underset{\cdot\cdot}{\text{Al}}}\overset{\overset{\cdot\cdot}{\text{Cl}}\text{:}}{\underset{\underset{\cdot\cdot}{\text{Cl}}\text{:}}{\text{:}}}\overset{\cdot\cdot}{\underset{\cdot\cdot}{\text{Cl}}}\text{:}\right]^{-1} \quad (1)
$$

base · · · · acid · · · · · · · acid

According to the Lewis concept of acids and bases the catalyst in this reaction behaves as an acid and the halide reacts as a base. Many other metallic halides catalyze the reaction in a similar manner. All of them can be shown to be acids by titrating with indicators in the proper solvent.

Simons and Archer [5] report the use of hydrogen fluoride as the catalyzing agent. They [6] found that the tertiary halides react readily at 0° C., the secondary halides require a temperature of 25° C., but the primary halides react only at higher temperatures (80° C.), thereby affording an approximation of the relative acid characteristics of the alkyl groups. The reactivity of the above halides is in agreement with other data on the electrophilic properties of these alkyl groups.[7, 8]

[1] Price, *Chem. Revs.*, **29**, 37 (1941).
[2] Bodendorf and Bohme, *Ann.*, **516**, 1 (1935).
[3] Wertyporoch and Firla, *Ann.*, **500**, 287 (1933).
[4] Fairbrother, *J. Chem. Soc.*, **1945**, 503.
[5] Simons and Archer, *J. Am. Chem. Soc.*, **60**, 986 (1938).
[6] Simons and Archer, *J. Am. Chem. Soc.*, **60**, 2953 (1938).
[7] Fittig, *Ann.*, **283**, 85 (1894).
[8] Euler and Lovgren, *Z. anorg. allgem. Chem.*, **147**, 123 (1925).

The "positive fragments" formed as a result of these acid-base reactions alkylate aromatic compounds through an electrophilic mechanism [9] involving the electron-deficient carbonium ion (R^+).

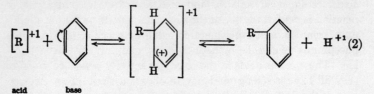

acid   base

Wohl and Wertyporoch [10] have reported that boron trifluoride will not catalyze the alkylation of benzene by alkyl chlorides. Hennion and Kurtz [11] have found that the presence of water or alcohol helps the reaction as follows:

$$H:\overset{..}{\underset{H}{O}}: + \overset{F}{\underset{F}{\overset{..}{B}}}:F \rightleftarrows H:\overset{..}{\underset{H}{O}}:\overset{F}{\underset{F}{\overset{..}{B}}}:F \rightleftarrows \left[H:\overset{..}{O}:\overset{F}{\underset{F}{\overset{..}{B}}}:F \right]^{-1} + H^{+1} \qquad (3)$$

base   acid   acid

$$H^{+1} + R:\overset{..}{\underset{..}{Cl}}: \rightleftarrows R:\overset{..}{\underset{..}{Cl}}:H^{+1} \rightleftarrows [R]^{+1} + H:\overset{..}{\underset{..}{Cl}}: \qquad (4)$$

acid   base   acid

Burwell and Archer [12] report that, although the alkyl chlorides and bromides are not catalyzed by boron trifluoride, the alkyl fluorides will react vigorously. They attribute this reactivity to the greater stability of the BF_4^{-1} ion as contrasted with the BF_3Br^{-1} ion or the BF_3Cl^{-1} ion.

OLEFINS. Olefins can be employed for the alkylation of aromatic compounds by using acid catalysts such as hydrogen fluoride,[13] sulfuric acid,[14] phosphoric acid,[15] phosphorus pentoxide,[16] boron trifluoride,[17, 18, 19] and aluminum chloride.[20, 21]

[9] Price, *Chem. Revs.*, **29**, 40 (1941).
[10] Wohl and Wertyporoch, *Ber.*, **64**, 1360 (1931).
[11] Hennion and Kurtz, *J. Am. Chem. Soc.*, **65**, 1001 (1943).
[12] Burwell and Archer, *J. Am. Chem. Soc.*, **64**, 1032 (1942).
[13] Simons and Archer, *J. Am. Chem. Soc.*, **60**, 2952 (1938).
[14] Ipatieff, Corson, and Pines, *J. Am. Chem. Soc.*, **58**, 919 (1936).
[15] Ipatieff, Pines, and Komarewsky, *Ind. Eng. Chem.*, **28**, 222 (1936).
[16] Truffault, *Compt. rend.*, **202**, 1286 (1936).
[17] Ipatieff and Grosse, *J. Am. Chem. Soc.*, **58**, 2339 (1936).
[18] Slanina and Sowa, *J. Am. Chem. Soc.*, **57**, 1547 (1935).
[19] Wunderly, Sowa, and Nieuwland, *J. Am. Chem. Soc.*, **58**, 1007 (1936).
[20] Hunter and Yohe, *J. Am. Chem. Soc.*, **55**, 1248 (1933).
[21] Price and Ciskowski, *J. Am. Chem. Soc.*, **60**, 2499 (1938).

The condensation of olefins with aromatic compounds can be explained through an electrophilic mechanism involving the acid-base concept. The electrophilic (acidic) catalyst reacts with the electrodotic (basic) olefin to form an acidic intermediate [20, 21] which can react with the aromatic compound which is electrodotic. The reactions seem to be:

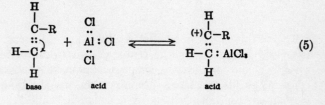

$$(5)$$

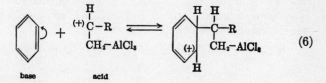

$$(6)$$

$$(7)$$

ALCOHOLS. Toussaint and Hennion [22] alkylated benzene with alcohols, using boron trifluoride as the acid catalyst and phosphorus pentoxide, sulfuric acid, and benzenesulfonic acid as assistants. They explained the mechanism on the basis of a dehydration of the alcohol to an olefin:

$$(8)$$

$$\begin{array}{ccc} CH_3 & & CH_3 \\ | & P_2O_5 & | \\ CH_2 & \xrightarrow{} & C-H \\ | & & :: \\ CH_2-OH & H-C \\ & & | \\ & & H \end{array}$$

[22] Toussaint and Hennion, *J. Am. Chem. Soc.*, **62**, 1145 (1940).

The electrophilic catalyst (BF$_3$) coordinates with the electrodotic olefin:

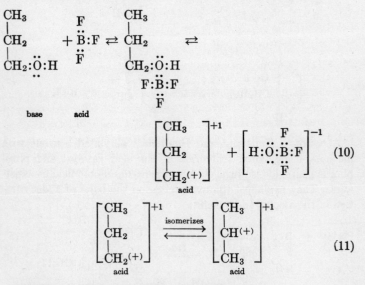

$$\tag{9}$$

The addition compound that results is an acid because of the low electron density on the center carbon of the olefin. This strongly acidic coordination compound can make a substance like benzene behave as a base. The alkylation would next involve a mechanism [23] such as that shown in equations 6 and 7. The fact that benzyl alcohol can be used to give diphenylmethane,[24] however, seems to indicate that the mechanism involving olefin formation as a preliminary step is not likely.

A preferable mechanism [25, 26, 27] would seem to be as follows:

$$\tag{10}$$

$$\tag{11}$$

[23] Pfeiffer and Wizinger, *Ann.*, **461**, 132 (1928).
[24] Simons and Archer, *J. Am. Chem. Soc.*, **62**, 1623 (1940).
[25] McKenna and Sowa, *J. Am. Chem. Soc.*, **59**, 470 (1937).
[26] Monacelli and Hennion, *J. Am. Chem. Soc.*, **63**, 1722 (1941).
[27] Welch and Hennion, *J. Am. Chem. Soc.*, **63**, 2063 (1941).

The electrodotic (basic) alcohol reacts with the electrophilic (acidic) catalyst to form an addition compound that is capable of ionizing.[26] The *n*-propyl carbonium ion (positive fragment) isomerizes to form the isopropyl ion.[28] The function of the catalyst is to produce a relatively high concentration of these positive fragments which can react with a benzenoid compound to produce an alkylated product as follows:

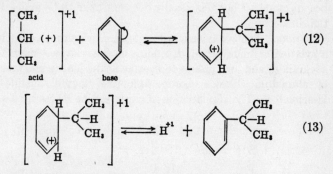

$$\begin{bmatrix} CH_3 \\ | \\ CH \ (+) \\ | \\ CH_3 \end{bmatrix}^{+1} \text{(acid)} + \bigcirc \text{(base)} \rightleftharpoons \begin{bmatrix} \bigcirc_{(+)} \\ \end{bmatrix}^{+1} \quad (12)$$

$$\begin{bmatrix} \end{bmatrix}^{+1} \rightleftharpoons H^{+1} + \quad (13)$$

The catalyst is regenerated by the following reaction:

$$\begin{bmatrix} F \\ H:\ddot{O}:\ddot{B}:F \\ \ddot{F} \end{bmatrix}^{-1} + H^{+1} \rightleftharpoons \begin{matrix} F \\ H:\ddot{O}:\ddot{B}:F \\ \ddot{H}\ \ddot{F} \end{matrix} \quad (14)$$

ETHERS. The catalytic effect of boron trifluoride on alkylations with ethers [23, 26, 29, 30] involves an acid-base reaction between boron trifluoride and ether.[26] That this is a true acid-base reaction can be readily demonstrated by titrations in different solvents and with various indicators.[31] The positive fragment that results from the ionization then reacts with the benzene, as previously described.

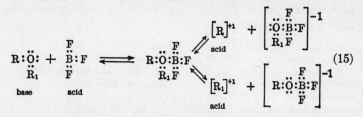

$$R:\ddot{O}: + \ddot{B}:F \rightleftharpoons R:\ddot{O}:\ddot{B}:F \quad (15)$$

[28] Whitmore, *J. Am. Chem. Soc.*, **54**, 3274 (1932).
[29] Ramser and Wiberg, *Ber.*, **63B**, 1136 (1930).
[30] O'Connor and Sowa, *J. Am. Chem. Soc.*, **60**, 125 (1938).
[31] Luder, McGuire, and Zuffanti, *J. Chem. Education*, **20**, 344 (1943).

Hydrogen fluoride [24] has also been used to catalyze these reactions. Whether or not the acid contains hydrogen, the behavior is essentially the same. The acid accepts a share in a pair of electrons from the base to form a coordinate bond. Ionization into single ions may then occur if the dielectric constant is high enough and the ions can be solvated. In media of very low dielectric constant considerable association into higher ionic multiples is to be expected,[32-35] but this usually does not have to be indicated in the equations.

ESTERS. The behavior of esters toward acids may result in an alkylation or an acylation, depending on the relative tendencies of acyl, alkyl, and aryl groups to become acidic ions in the presence of aluminum chloride, boron trifluoride, metallic halides, or H-acids.[36-38] The alkylation mechanism can be represented as:

$$
\begin{array}{c}
\overset{\text{O}}{\underset{\underset{\ddot{\text{R}}'}{\|}}{\text{R}-\ddot{\text{C}}:\ddot{\text{O}}:}} + \overset{\text{F}}{\underset{\ddot{\ddot{\text{F}}}}{\ddot{\text{B}}:\text{F}}} \rightleftarrows \overset{\text{O}}{\underset{\underset{\ddot{\text{R}}'}{\|}}{\text{R}-\ddot{\text{C}}:\ddot{\text{O}}:}}\overset{\text{F}}{\underset{\ddot{\text{F}}}{\ddot{\text{B}}:\text{F}}} \rightleftarrows
\end{array}
$$

base   acid

$$
[\text{R}']^{+1} + \left[\ \overset{\text{O}}{\underset{\underset{\ddot{\text{F}}}{\|}}{\text{R}-\ddot{\text{C}}:\ddot{\text{O}}:\ddot{\text{B}}:\text{F}}}\ \right]^{-1} \tag{16}
$$

acid

The acyl group, being more electrophilic than the alkyl (R′) group, will not be released,[36-38] and, therefore, in the presence of an aromatic compound an alkylation will result.

However, if R′ is an aryl group which is more strongly electrophilic, the acyl group will be released as a carbonium ion [39, 40] and acylation will result. This reaction is discussed further under the section on acylation.

[32] Fuoss and Kraus, J. Am. Chem. Soc., 55, 3614 (1933).
[33] Fuoss and Kraus, J. Am. Chem. Soc., 55, 2387 (1933).
[34] Luder, Kraus, Kraus, and Fuoss, J. Am. Chem. Soc., 58, 255 (1936).
[35] Vernon, Luder, and Giella, J. Am. Chem. Soc., 63, 862 (1941).
[36] Bowden, J. Am. Chem. Soc., 60, 645 (1938).
[37] McKenna and Sowa, J. Am. Chem. Soc., 59, 1204 (1937).
[38] Norris and Arthur, J. Am. Chem. Soc., 62, 874 (1940).
[39] Brown, J. Am. Chem. Soc., 61, 1483 (1939).
[40] Whitmore and Bernstein, J. Am. Chem. Soc., 60, 2626 (1938).

The following mechanism has been suggested for the alkylation[41] catalyzed by hydrogen fluoride:

$$
\begin{array}{c}
O \\
\parallel \\
R\!-\!C\!:\!\ddot{O}: \\
\vert \\
\dot{R}'
\end{array}
+ H\!:\!\ddot{F}: \rightleftarrows
\left[
\begin{array}{c}
O \\
\parallel \\
R\!-\!C\!:\!\ddot{O}\!:\!H \\
\vert \\
\dot{R}'
\end{array}
\right]^{+1}
+ \left[\,:\!\ddot{F}\!:\,\right]^{-1} \qquad (17)
$$

base   acid

$$
\left[
\begin{array}{c}
O \\
\parallel \\
R\!-\!C\!:\!\ddot{O}\!:\!H \\
\vert \\
\dot{R}'
\end{array}
\right]^{+1}
\rightleftarrows [R']^{+1} +
\begin{array}{c}
O \\
\parallel \\
R\!-\!C\!:\!\ddot{O}\!:\!H
\end{array}
\qquad (18)
$$

acid

Again the action of the catalyst is essentially the same whether hydrogen is present or not. The same positive fragments are produced by the catalyst.

ALLYLIC GROUPS. Simons and Archer [42] investigated the alkylation of benzene using benzyl chloride, cinnamic acid, and allyl alcohol as the alkylating agents and hydrogen fluoride as the acid catalyst. The products they obtained are in agreement with those that might be predicted on the basis of the polarization or polarizability of the alkylating agents. Boron trifluoride, stannic chloride, and other acid catalysts also will catalyze these alkylations. Possible mechanisms might be as follows:

1. *Benzyl chloride.*

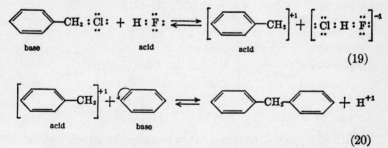

(19)

(20)

[41] Simons, Archer, and Randall, *J. Am. Chem. Soc.*, **61**, 1821 (1939).
[42] Simons and Archer, *J. Am. Chem. Soc.*, **61**, 1521 (1939).

2. *Cinnamic acid.*

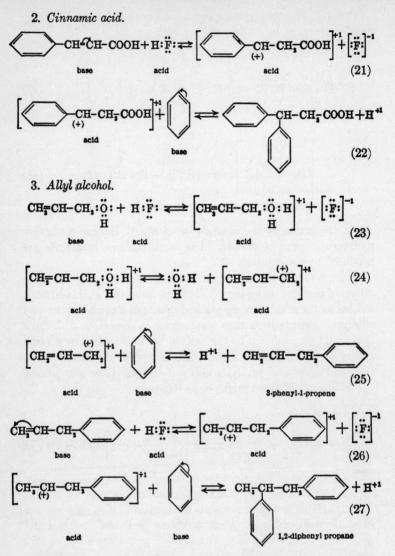

With allyl alcohol the first point of electrophilic attack is at the carbon-oxygen bond, thus producing an allyl carbonium ion which will attack a benzene molecule to produce the 3-phenyl-1-propene. This product is very susceptible to electrophilic attack by the catalyst because of the polarization of the molecule. Thus a carbonium ion is produced which can react with benzene to form 1,2-diphenylpropane. The polarization indicated is supported by the fact that practically no 1,3-diphenylpropane is formed in the reaction.

The use of sulfuric acid as an electrophilic catalyst produces much larger amounts of the 1,2-diphenylpropane and less of the 3-phenyl-1-propene, probably because H_2SO_4 is a stronger acid.

3. Acylations.

ESTERS. Acylation by aromatic esters,[36, 39, 40, 43, 44] mentioned in a preceding section, can be catalyzed by aluminum chloride, boron trifluoride, metallic halides, and H-acids as catalysts. The possible mechanism is represented by the following equations:

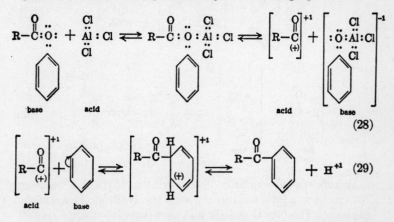

$$(28)$$

$$(29)$$

The positive fragment released from the ester, by reaction with the acid catalyst, is the $\left(R-C \overset{O}{\diagup} \right)^{+1}$ group.[39, 40] The formation of the fragment represents a displacement of one acid by another. The $(C_6H_5)^{+1}$ group is not split off because it is a stronger acid than the acyl carbonium ion. Equation 29 shows the usual electrophilic attack that results in substitution in the benzenoid compound.

Aromatic esters will undergo a rearrangement (Fries reaction) to produce *ortho-* and *para-*hydroxyketones [45] when treated with

[43] Cox, *J. Am. Chem. Soc.*, **52**, 352 (1930).
[44] Kane and Lowy, *J. Am. Chem. Soc.*, **58**, 2605 (1936).
[45] Blatt, *Chem. Revs.*, **27**, 429 (1940).

acidic catalysts such as $AlCl_3$ or $ZnCl_2$. In view of our preceding discussion, this reaction is not surprising and can be explained readily as an acid-base reaction:

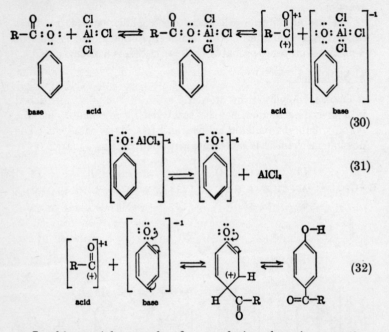

(30)

(31)

(32)

In this special example of an acylation there is a reaction between the acidic acyl group and the electrodotic aromatic nucleus. The fact that *ortho* and *para* derivatives are obtained can readily be explained on the basis of increased electron density at these positions, an increase that facilitates the electrophilic attack of the carbonium ion.

CARBOXY COMPOUNDS. Carboxy compounds [46] have been employed for acylations using hydrogen fluoride as a catalyst:

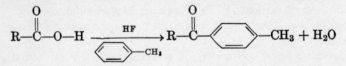

[46] Simons, Randall, and Archer, *J. Am. Chem. Soc.*, **61**, 1795 (1939).

Simons [47] reports that carboxylic acids dissolved in liquid hydrogen fluoride produce conducting solutions:

$$
\underset{\substack{\text{base}}}{R-\overset{\displaystyle O}{\overset{\|}{C}}:\ddot{O}:H} + \underset{\text{acid}}{HF} \rightleftarrows \left[R-\overset{\displaystyle O}{\overset{\|}{C}}:\overset{..}{\underset{\displaystyle \ddot{H}}{O}}:H \right]^{+1} + F^{-1} \qquad (33)
$$

The resulting cation will then dissociate to form water and the acyl carbonium ion, which will acylate an aromatic compound through an electrophilic attack:

$$
\left[R-\overset{\displaystyle O}{\overset{\|}{C}}:\overset{..}{\underset{\displaystyle \ddot{H}}{O}}:H \right]^{+1} \rightleftarrows \left[R-\underset{(+)}{\overset{\displaystyle O}{\overset{\|}{C}}} \right]^{+1} + :\overset{..}{\underset{\displaystyle \ddot{H}}{O}}:H \qquad (34)
$$

It will be noted that these weak carboxylic acids are being forced to act as bases by the much stronger acids used as catalysts.

ACYL HALIDES. The mechanism of the acylation reaction of the acid halides [47] can be explained on the basis of the following equation:

$$
\underset{\substack{\text{base}}}{R-\overset{\displaystyle O}{\overset{\|}{C}}:\overset{..}{\underset{..}{Cl}}:} + \underset{\text{acid}}{H^{+1}} \rightleftarrows \underset{\text{acid}}{\left[R-\underset{(+)}{\overset{\displaystyle O}{\overset{\|}{C}}} \right]^{+1}} + H:\overset{..}{\underset{..}{Cl}}: \qquad (35)
$$

CARBOXY ANHYDRIDES. The mechanism of the acid-catalyzed acylations using a carboxy anhydride as the acylating agent could be written as follows:

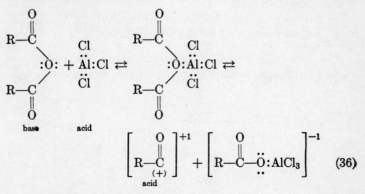

$$
\left[R-\underset{(+)}{\overset{\displaystyle O}{\overset{\|}{C}}} \right]^{+1} + \left[R-\overset{\displaystyle O}{\overset{\|}{C}}-\overset{..}{\underset{..}{O}}:AlCl_3 \right]^{-1} \qquad (36)
$$

---

[47] Simons, *Chem. Revs.*, **8**, 213 (1931).

The positive fragments formed in these reactions will acylate benzenoid systems through a reaction mechanism such as that shown in equation 29.

4. Esterification of Aldehydes (Cannizzaro Reaction).

A special example of the Cannizzaro reaction results in the direct formation of an ester from two molecules of an aldehyde.[48, 49] The catalytic agent used here is an acid (aluminum alkoxide) according to the Lewis theory. This acid coordinates with a molecule of the aldehyde, acting as a base, and produces an acidic intermediate, as follows:

$$
\begin{array}{ccc}
\text{H} & \text{R} & \text{H} \quad \text{R} \\
| & | & | \quad | \\
\text{R—C::Ö:} + \text{Al—O—R} & \rightleftarrows & \text{R—C:Ö:Al—O—R} \\
& | & \underset{(+)}{} \quad | \\
& \text{O} & \text{O} \\
& | & | \\
& \text{R} & \text{R}
\end{array}
\qquad (37)
$$

base   acid   acid

A small amount of the aldehyde is probably already present in its reactive form:

$$
\begin{array}{c}
\text{H} \\
| \\
\underset{(+)}{\text{R—C}}\text{:Ö:}^{(-)}
\end{array}
$$

The function of the catalyst seems to be to increase the concentration of the reactive form that has an electrophilic carbonyl carbon as shown in equation 37.

The next step has been considered the removal of a hydride ion from a second molecule of the aldehyde as follows:

$$
\begin{array}{cc}
\text{H} & \text{O} \\
| & \| \\
\underset{(+)}{\text{R—C}}\text{—O} \rightarrow \text{Al(OR)}_3 + \text{R'—C} & \rightleftarrows \\
& \text{H}
\end{array}
$$

acid   base

$$
\left[
\begin{array}{c}
\text{H} \\
| \\
\text{R—C—O—Al(OR)}_3 \\
| \\
\text{H}
\end{array}
\right]^{-1}
+
\left[
\begin{array}{c}
\text{O} \\
\| \\
\underset{(+)}{\text{R'—C}}
\end{array}
\right]^{+1}
\qquad (38)
$$

base   acid

[48] Child and Adkins, *J. Am. Chem. Soc.*, **45**, 3013 (1923).
[49] Tischtschenko, *Chem. Zentr.*, **77**, 1309, 1552 (1906).

The final step involves the displacement of one acid by another.

$$[R\text{---}CH_2\text{---}O\text{---}Al(OR)_3]^{-1} + \left[\begin{array}{c} O \\ \parallel \\ R'\text{---}C \\ (+) \end{array}\right]^{+1} \rightleftarrows$$

base   acid

$$R\text{---}CH_2\text{---}O\overset{\overset{\textstyle O}{\parallel}}{\text{---}C}\text{---}R' + Al(OR)_3 \quad (39)$$

5. Condensation Reactions of Carbonyl Compounds.

The reactions of aldehydes with hydroxylamine, hydrazines, and semicarbazides are catalyzed by acids. These reaction mechanisms can be explained in terms of the new terminology.

The acid catalyst coordinates with the carbonyl oxygen,[50, 51] which is electrodotic:

$$R\overset{\overset{\textstyle :\ddot{O}_{\text{)}}}{\underset{\textstyle R}{\overset{\displaystyle |}{|}}}{\ddot{C}} + HA \rightleftarrows \left[\begin{array}{c} :\ddot{O}:H \\ | \\ R\text{---}\ddot{C}(+) \\ | \\ R \end{array}\right]^{+1} + A^{-1} \quad (40)$$

base   acid   acid

The resulting carbonium ion behaves as an acid and thus coordinates with the electrodotic nitrogen of the above-mentioned compounds. For example, with the semicarbazide the following reactions will take place:

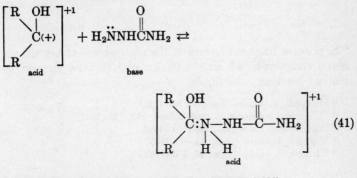

[50] Conant and Bartlett, *J. Am. Chem. Soc.*, **54**, 2881 (1932).
[51] Westheimer, *J. Am. Chem. Soc.*, **56**, 1962 (1934).

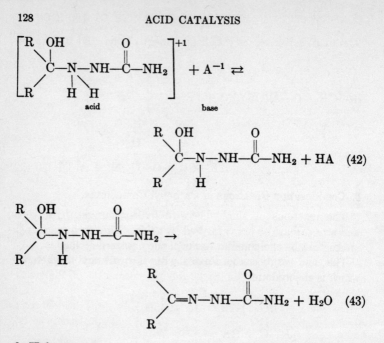

$$\left[\begin{array}{c} R \\ \diagdown \\ R \diagup \end{array} \begin{array}{c} OH \\ | \\ C-N-NH-\overset{O}{\overset{||}{C}}-NH_2 \\ \overset{|}{H} \overset{|}{H} \end{array}\right]^{+1} + A^{-1} \rightleftarrows$$

acid   base

$$\begin{array}{c} R \\ \diagdown \\ R \diagup \end{array} \begin{array}{c} OH \\ | \\ C-N-NH-\overset{O}{\overset{||}{C}}-NH_2 + HA \\ \overset{|}{H} \end{array} \quad (42)$$

$$\begin{array}{c} R \\ \diagdown \\ R \diagup \end{array} \begin{array}{c} OH \\ | \\ C-N-NH-\overset{O}{\overset{||}{C}}-NH_2 \rightarrow \\ \overset{|}{H} \end{array}$$

$$\begin{array}{c} R \\ \diagdown \\ R \diagup \end{array} C=N-NH-\overset{O}{\overset{||}{C}}-NH_2 + H_2O \quad (43)$$

6. Halogenation.

AROMATIC COMPOUNDS. The halogenation [52-56] of aromatic compounds probably has a mechanism similar to that of the Friedel-Crafts reactions:

$$:\!\overset{\cdot\cdot}{Br}\!:\!\overset{\cdot\cdot}{Br}\!: + \overset{:\overset{\cdot\cdot}{Br}:}{\underset{:\overset{\cdot\cdot}{Br}:}{Fe}}\!:\!\overset{\cdot\cdot}{Br}\!: \rightleftarrows \left[:\overset{\cdot\cdot}{Br}\right]^{+1} + \left[\begin{array}{c} :\overset{\cdot\cdot}{Br}: \\ :\overset{\cdot\cdot}{Br}:Fe:\overset{\cdot\cdot}{Br}: \\ :\overset{\cdot\cdot}{Br}: \end{array}\right]^{-1} \quad (44)$$

base   acid   acid   base

The positive fragment formed in the reaction will attack the aromatic compound and cause substitution [9] to take place in the manner previously described:

[52] Meerwein, Z. angew. Chem., **38**, 815 (1925).
[53] Pfeiffer and Schneider, J. prakt. Chem., **129**, 129 (1931).
[54] Price, J. Am. Chem. Soc., **58**, 2101 (1936).
[55] Wizinger, Z. angew. Chem., **44**, 469 (1931).
[56] Wizinger, Z. angew. Chem., **46**, 756 (1933).

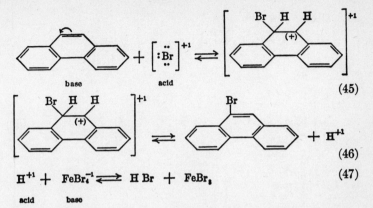

$$H^{+1} + FeBr_4^{-1} \rightleftharpoons HBr + FeBr_3 \qquad (47)$$

acid   base

Other acidic compounds like antimony pentachloride, stannic chloride, and iodine can catalyze the reaction through the hetero-fission of the bromine molecule and the formation of the polar complex.

Benzene can be iodinated under anhydrous conditions with silver perchlorate as a catalyst.[57, 58] One suggested mechanism is:

$$:\overset{..}{\underset{..}{I}}:\overset{..}{\underset{..}{I}}: + AgClO_4 \rightarrow Ag:\overset{..}{\underset{..}{I}}: + ClO_4^{-1} + \left[:\overset{..}{\underset{..}{I}}\right]^{+1} \qquad (48)$$

base   acid   acid

Such a simple ionic equation is probably inadequate because of the high ionic association observed in benzene.[59] However, there is no doubt that silver ion is acidic, as shown by its behavior in forming complexes in water and by its effect on indicators in other solvents.[60]

ALCOHOLS. The catalytic action of zinc chloride on the conversion of alcohols to halides is well known. The catalyst used is an acid which coordinates with the basic alcohol. An α,γ-shift of the chlorine atom accounts for the formation of the organic halide.[61]

$$R:\overset{..}{O}: + H:\overset{..}{\underset{..}{Cl}}: \rightleftharpoons \left[R:\overset{..}{O}:H\right]^{+1} + \left[:\overset{..}{\underset{..}{Cl}}:\right]^{-1} \qquad (49)$$
$$\overset{}{\underset{H}{}} \qquad\qquad\qquad \overset{}{\underset{H}{}}$$

base   acid   acid   base

[57] Birkenbach and Goubeau, *Ber.*, **67B**, 917 (1934).
[58] Birkenbach and Goubeau, *Ber.*, **65B**, 395 (1932).
[59] Truffault, *Compt. rend.*, **202**, 1286 (1936).
[60] Lewis, *J. Franklin Inst.*, **226**, 293 (1938).
[61] Lucas, *J. Am. Chem. Soc.*, **52**, 803 (1930).

$$R\!:\!\overset{\displaystyle ..}{\underset{\displaystyle H}{O}}\!: \; + \; \overset{..}{Zn}\!:\!\overset{..}{\underset{..}{Cl}}\!: \; + \; \left[\,:\!\overset{..}{\underset{..}{Cl}}\!:\,\right]^{-1} \; \rightleftharpoons \; \left[\begin{array}{c} :\!\overset{..}{\underset{..}{Cl}}\!: \\ R\!:\!\overset{..}{O}\!:\!\overset{..}{Zn}\!:\!\overset{..}{Cl}\!: \\ \overset{..}{H} \; :\!\overset{..}{\underset{..}{Cl}}\!: \end{array}\right]^{-1} \qquad (50)$$

base   acid   base

$$\left[\begin{array}{c} \overset{\frown}{\;\;}:\!\overset{..}{\underset{..}{Cl}}\!: \\ R\!:\!\overset{..}{O}\!: \; \overset{..}{Zn} \; :\!\overset{..}{\underset{..}{Cl}}\!: \\ \overset{..}{H} \; :\!\overset{..}{\underset{..}{Cl}}\!: \end{array}\right]^{-1} \; \rightleftharpoons \; R\!:\!\overset{..}{\underset{..}{Cl}}\!: \; + \; \left[\begin{array}{c} :\!\overset{..}{O}\!: \; Zn \; :\!\overset{..}{\underset{..}{Cl}}\!: \\ \overset{..}{H} \; :\!\overset{..}{\underset{..}{Cl}}\!: \end{array}\right]^{-1} \qquad (51)$$

$$\left[\begin{array}{c} :\!\overset{..}{O}\!: \; Zn \; :\!\overset{..}{\underset{..}{Cl}}\!: \\ \overset{..}{H} \; :\!\overset{..}{\underset{..}{Cl}}\!: \end{array}\right]^{-1} + \; H^{+1} \; \rightarrow \; ZnCl_2 + H_2O \qquad (51a)$$

7. Hydrolysis.

The hydrolysis of benzyl chloride is catalyzed by the presence of Hg^{+2} salts.[62] The electrophilic Hg^{+2} salts are here behaving as acids and react with the organic halide to form a carbonium ion:

$$\langle\!\!\!\!\bigcirc\!\!\!\!\rangle\!\!-\!CH_2\!:\!\overset{..}{\underset{..}{Cl}}\!: \; + \; Hg^{+2} \; \rightarrow$$

base   acid

$$\left[\langle\!\!\!\!\bigcirc\!\!\!\!\rangle\!\!-\!CH_2\right]^{+1} + \; \left[Hg\!:\!\overset{..}{\underset{..}{Cl}}\!:\right]^{+1} \qquad (52)$$

acid   acid

$$\left[\langle\!\!\!\!\bigcirc\!\!\!\!\rangle\!\!-\!CH_2\right]^{+1} + \; H\!:\!\overset{..}{\underset{..}{O}}\!:\!H \; \rightarrow$$

acid   base

$$\langle\!\!\!\!\bigcirc\!\!\!\!\rangle\!\!-\!CH_2\!:\!\overset{..}{\underset{..}{O}}\!:\!H \; + \; H^{+1} \qquad (53)$$

We see here the familiar reaction of the acid catalyst, i.e., the displacing of one acid by another. The reaction rate is increased by the catalyst because the Hg^{+2} ions increase the concentration of benzyl carbonium ions. The result is a speeding up of the reaction shown in equation 53.

8. Sulfonation and Nitration.

Boron trifluoride has been reported as an acid catalyst in sulfonation and nitration reactions.[63] The amounts of catalyst required

[62] Roberts and Hammett, *J. Am. Chem. Soc.*, **59**, 1063 (1937).
[63] Thomas, Anzilotti, and Hennion, *Ind. Eng. Chem.*, **32**, 408 (1940).

indicated that the reaction proceeds as follows:

$$RH + HOSO_2OH + BF_3 \rightarrow R-SO_2OH + H_2O:BF_3 \quad (54)$$

$$RH + HONO_2 + BF_3 \rightarrow R-NO_2 + H_2O:BF_3 \quad (55)$$

Since the rate of sulfonation increases with increasing acid concentration in sulfuric acid of less than 100 per cent concentration and with the concentration of sulfur trioxide in fuming acid,[64-66] the sulfonation probably takes place largely through the typically acidic displacement of a proton by the acid, SO_3. (See page 63.)

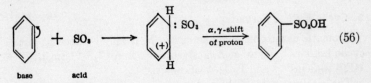

The catalytic function of the boron trifluoride may be to increase the concentration of the sulfur trioxide by combining with the water to form $H_2O:BF_3$.

$$H_2SO_4 + BF_3 \rightarrow SO_3 + H_2O:BF_3 \quad (57)$$

The actual mechanism of *nitration* is not known, but it may possibly involve the NO_2^{+1} ion [67] as follows:

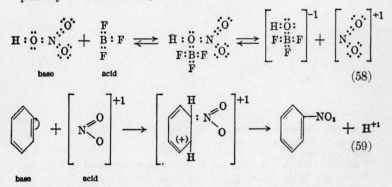

The catalytic function of the boron trifluoride may be to produce a higher concentration of the NO_2^{+1} ions according to equation 58.

[64] Martinsen, *Z. physik. Chem.*, **62**, 713 (1908).
[65] Pinnow, *Z. Elektrochem.*, **21**, 380 (1915).
[66] Pinnow, *Z. Elektrochem.*, **23**, 243 (1917).
[67] Price, *Chem. Revs.*, **29**, 51 (1941).

Hydrogen fluoride has been reported as having a strong catalytic effect on sulfonation and nitration reactions.[68]

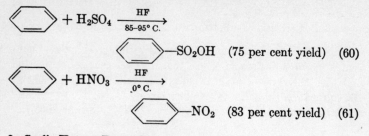

$$\langle\,\rangle + H_2SO_4 \xrightarrow[85-95° C.]{HF}$$

$$\langle\,\rangle—SO_2OH \quad \text{(75 per cent yield)} \quad (60)$$

$$\langle\,\rangle + HNO_3 \xrightarrow[.0° C.]{HF}$$

$$\langle\,\rangle—NO_2 \quad \text{(83 per cent yield)} \quad (61)$$

9. Cyclic Ketone Formation.

Aromatic carboxylic compounds can be readily cyclized to form cyclic ketones. Many acid catalysts such as $AlCl_3$,[69–72] $SnCl_4$,[73–76] HF,[77] H_2SO_4,[78, 79] and P_2O_5 [80] can be used.

The catalytic effects observed in these reactions can be explained readily as instances of simple acid-base catalysis if one adopts the conception of acids and bases proposed by G. N. Lewis. One specific example is the condensation of o-benzoylbenzoic acid to anthraquinone, which has been studied by several authors without arriving at a completely satisfactory explanation of the effects observed.

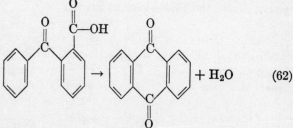

$$→ \quad + H_2O \qquad (62)$$

[68] Simons, Passino, and Archer, *J. Am. Chem. Soc.*, **63**, 608 (1941).
[69] Mayer and Stamm, *Ber.*, **56**, 1424 (1923).
[70] Kipping and Hill, *J. Chem. Soc.*, 1899, 144.
[71] Martin and Fieser, *Org. Syntheses, Coll. Vol.* **2**, 569 (1943).
[72] Vollmann, Becker, Corell, and Streeck, *Ann.*, **531**, 1 (1937).
[73] Winterstein, Vetter, and Schön, *Ber.*, **68**, 1079 (1935).
[74] Fieser and Fieser, *J. Am. Chem. Soc.*, **57**, 782 (1935).
[75] Fieser, Hershberg, Long, and Newman, *J. Am. Chem. Soc.*, **59**, 475 (1937).
[76] Bachmann, Carmack, and Safir, *J. Am. Chem. Soc.*, **63**, 1682 (1941).
[77] Fieser and Hershberg, *J. Am. Chem. Soc.*, **61**, 1272 (1939).
[78] Cook and Hewett, *J. Chem. Soc.*, 1934, 365.
[79] Horne and Shriner, *J. Am. Chem. Soc.*, **55**, 4652 (1933).
[80] Cook and Hewett, *J. Chem. Soc.*, 1933, 398.

Deane and Huffman [81] have extended rate measurements of the o-benzoylbenzoic acid condensation into oleum of concentrations up to 29 per cent SO_3 at 75 and 85°. They found that the velocity constant increased steadily up to their maximum sulfur trioxide percentage.

This increase in reaction rate with increased concentration of sulfur trioxide in sulfuric acid is readily understood when considered from the Lewis viewpoint. It is merely due to increased overall acidity. Sulfur trioxide is a stronger acid than sulfuric acid. Lewis and Bigeleisen [82] have shown that the acidity of sulfuric acid solutions increases with concentration of sulfur trioxide. Close correlation is evident in comparing the Lewis and Bigeleisen plot of Hammett's acidity function with the plot of variation in reaction rate with concentration of sulfur trioxide given by Deane and Huffman.[81] This close correlation indicates that the condensation of o-benzoylbenzoic acid is an acid-catalyzed reaction, and that the reaction rate does not depend upon a particular species but rather upon the acid strength. Probably SO_3, H_2SO_4, and H_3O^{+1} are the three principal species involved, but the question of the exact proportion is unimportant, since the overall acidity can be measured experimentally. Of course it is obvious that in 65 per cent oleum the ratio of SO_3 to H_3O^{+1} is very great.

According to this viewpoint, the inhibiting effect of the product anthraquinone and of other substances can readily be explained. Anthraquinone is weakly basic. Each oxygen atom can donate a share in a pair of electrons to a sufficiently strong acid.[83] The presence of the anthraquinone in such a highly acidic medium simply decreases its acidity and, therefore, its effectiveness as a catalyst. A similar explanation applies to the other inhibitors tested by Deane and Huffman. Several of these substances such as $AlCl_3$, HCl, and $CuCl_2$ are typical generalized acid catalysts. Even these acids, strong enough to catalyze Friedel-Crafts and similar reactions, are forced to behave as weak bases by the stronger mixture of sulfur trioxide and sulfuric acid.

In view of this very great acidity of fuming sulfuric acid, the statement of Deane and Huffman that "The effect of definite added

[81] Deane and Huffman, *Ind. Eng. Chem.*, **35**, 684 (1943).
[82] Lewis and Bigeleisen, *J. Am. Chem. Soc.*, **65**, 1144 (1943).
[83] Ebert, *Z. Elektrochem.*, **31**, 113 (1925).

amounts of concentrated hydrofluoric acid will more fully indicate the status of this reaction as a case of acid-base catalysis" is not likely to be upheld. They themselves have already tried a stronger acid than HF, namely, $AlCl_3$, and found that it did not increase the reaction rate in fuming sulfuric acid but actually decreased it.

Newman [84] has postulated the formation of the cyclic carbonium ion

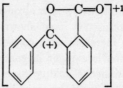

as the first step in the condensation. This suggestion is based on the formation of a quantity of pseudo ester when methyl alcohol was present. The cyclic ion is considered to be formed by the reaction of sulfuric acid on the o-benzoylbenzoic acid with H_3O^{+1} and $2HSO_4^{-1}$ as the other products. This explanation conforms to the Brønsted theory of acids and bases, but obviously the Brønsted theory cannot explain the large increase in velocity constant as the amount of sulfur trioxide is increased. On the other hand, the observed behavior is exactly what is expected on the basis of the electronic theory of acids and bases. Sulfur trioxide is a much stronger acid (i.e., has a greater tendency to appropriate lone electron pairs) than H_2SO_4 or H_3O^{+1}.

However, it is not assumed that the hypothesis of a cyclic ion is incorrect. The cyclic ion could be formed just as well by sulfur trioxide as by sulfuric acid

$$o\text{-benzoylbenzoic acid} + SO_3 \rightleftarrows [\text{cyclic ion}]^{+1} + HSO_4^{-1}$$

And so, whether the cyclic ion or some other explanation is adopted, the ability of the Lewis theory to explain the observed catalytic effects is not affected.

An alternative mechanism,[85] which we prefer for reasons discussed subsequently, is as follows:

[84] Newman, *J. Am. Chem. Soc.*, **64**, 2324 (1942).
[85] Luder and Zuffanti, *J. Am. Chem. Soc.*, **66**, 524 (1944).

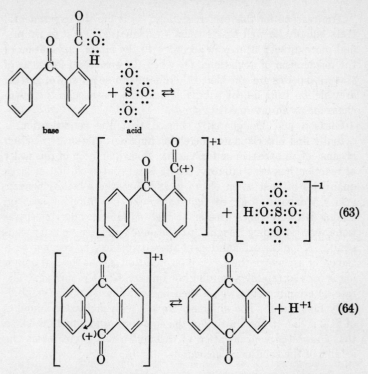

The use of H_2SO_4, H_3O^{+1}, or any other acid species present, in place of the sulfur trioxide, in the above equations would serve equally well since according to the Lewis theory acids coordinate with lone electron pairs. In equation 63 the sulfur trioxide behaves as a typical acid by coordinating with the oxygen electron pair to split off the OH^{-1} group, thus leaving the carbon atom electron-deficient. The coordination makes the carbon atom acidic, since it now has a great tendency to appropriate a lone electron pair to complete its octet again. The two possibilities are: the formation of the cyclic ion, and the formation of anthraquinone according to equation 64. Both reactions undoubtedly take place, since Newman seems to have demonstrated conclusively the existence of a large proportion of the cyclic ion at low temperatures. But, since the reaction under discussion is the formation of anthraquinone, it seems unnecessary to involve the cyclic ion. We prefer to regard its formation as a side reaction to, rather than the first step in, the production of anthraquinone.

The reasons for this preference are: (1) it fits the experimental facts equally as well as Newman's explanation; (2) it is simpler and more direct; (3) it is in accord with the newer explanation of the mechanism of acylations; (4) when the structural formulas of all three species are considered there seems to be no way of getting a cyclic ion from o-benzoylbenzoic acid except through the open-chain ion as an intermediate step.

Gleason and Dougherty [86] showed that the condensation is actually first order and not merely an apparent first-order reaction because of an excess of sulfuric acid. No explanation of this order of reaction has been offered. There is a rapid evolution of large quantities of heat when oleum is added to the o-benzoylbenzoic acid. We have observed that this rapid evolution of heat on mixing is many times greater at high sulfur trioxide concentrations, corresponding roughly to the much greater velocity constant. A logical explanation of these two facts in keeping with the other aspects of the Lewis interpretation is that the carbonium ion is formed rapidly according to equation 63 upon mixing. The rate-determining step would then be equation 64, which is obviously first order. The difference in rate with increasing amounts of SO_3 is due to the shifting of the equilibrium in equation 63, so that the initial concentration of carbonium ion is greater as the acidity of the solution is increased.

10. Summary.

In all the examples of acid catalysis considered in this chapter the characteristic effect of the acid catalyst is the increase in concentration of the acid group involved in the reaction. This is usually accomplished by the familiar displacement of one acid by another. In a few reactions displacement does not result, but the combination of the acid with the reacting substance merely localizes the electron deficiency on one atom, which can then behave as an acid. One example is alkylation by olefins.

Either way, the net result is the characteristic increase in the concentration of the acid group. The effect is similar whether the catalyst is an H-acid or any other acid.

[86] Gleason and Dougherty, *J. Am. Chem. Soc.*, **51**, 310 (1929)

BASE CATALYSIS

1. Introduction.

In this chapter it will be assumed that the characteristic effect of the basic catalyst is the increase in concentration of the basic group involved in the reaction. The mechanisms that bring about these changes will be discussed by means of well-known reactions.

The bases used as catalysts are electrodotic reagents that may be ions or molecules, e.g.,

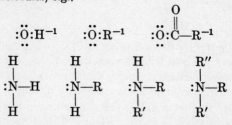

and $:C{\equiv}N:^{-1}$. These reagents are also recognized as bases, by the Brønsted theory, because they are proton acceptors. In this chapter, however, it will be shown that these bases *can* and *do* combine with many electrophilic (acidic) substances other than the proton. It will be evident that the proton is only one of many different electrophilic substances that exhibit acidic behavior.

2. Reactions of Carbonyl Compounds Containing α-H Atoms.

$$\left[R-CH_2-CHO \quad \text{or} \quad R-CH-CHO \atop \qquad\qquad\qquad\quad R' \right]$$

SELF-CONDENSATION. *Aldehydes* (aldol condensations). The synthetic importance of these condensations is known to all organic chemists. A wide variety of compounds can be prepared through the condensation of two carbonyl compounds. The catalysts used are bases such as acetates, carbonates, pyridine, and amines.[1] These catalytic agents are bases according to both the Lewis and the Brønsted theories. The mechanism [2] of the reaction may be represented as follows:

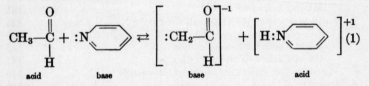

(1)

One base (pyridine) tends to displace the other from combination with the proton. This base (the carbanion) can then react with another molecule of the aldehyde which is thus behaving as an acid:

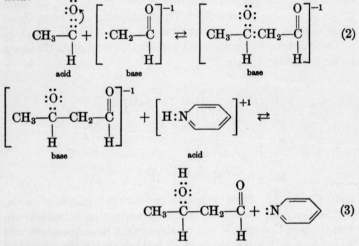

(2)

(3)

[1] Bell, *J. Chem. Soc.*, **1937**, 1637.

[2] Hammett, *Physical Organic Chemistry*, McGraw-Hill Book Co., New York, 1940, p. 343.

When the reaction is carried out in deuterium water [3] no deuterium hydrogen becomes attached to the carbon, indicating that water takes no direct part in the mechanism of the reaction.

Ketones (aldolization). The effect of basic catalysts on the active α-H atoms of ketones [4] is the same as that produced in aldehydes. The result is the displacement of one base by another base. The preparation of diacetone alcohol from acetone using $Ba(OH)_2$ as a catalyst, is familiar to organic chemists:[5]

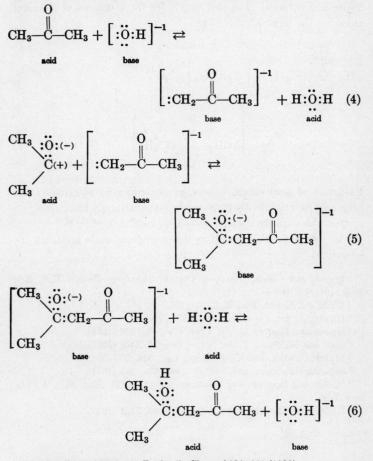

[3] Bonhoeffer and Walters, *Z. physik. Chem.*, **A181**, 441 (1938).
[4] LaMer and Miller, *J. Am. Chem. Soc.*, **57**, 2674 (1935).
[5] Koelichen. *Z. physik. Chem.*, **33**, 129 (1900).

The basic catalysts used in this type of reaction are OH^{-1}, ammonia, primary amines, and secondary amines.[4, 6] The basic catalyst displaces a basic anion from the ketone as shown in equation 4. The result is an increase in the reaction rate for the reaction shown by equation 5, i.e., the rate-determining step in this mechanism. Equation 6 shows the regeneration of the catalyst.

Esters (Claisen reaction). The Claisen reaction [7-10] probably involves an ionic mechanism similar to that shown for the aldehydes and ketones. The first step is the displacement of the ester anion by the basic alkoxide ion:

$$CH_3 - \overset{\overset{O}{\|}}{C} - OC_2H_5 + \left[:\overset{\cdot\cdot}{\underset{\cdot\cdot}{O}}:C_2H_5 \right]^{-1} \rightleftarrows$$

$$\text{acid} \qquad\qquad \text{base}$$

$$\left[:CH_2 - \overset{\overset{O}{\|}}{C} - OC_2H_5 \right]^{-1} + H:\overset{\cdot\cdot}{\underset{\cdot\cdot}{O}}:C_2H_5 \quad (7)$$

$$\text{base} \qquad\qquad \text{acid}$$

Evidence of ester anion formation according to equation 7 has been reported in the literature.[11, 12] Other strongly basic catalysts such as the triphenylmethyl carbanion can be used.[13, 14]

The rate-determining step in this condensation is probably the following:

[6] Branch and Calvin, *Theory of Organic Chemistry*, Prentice-Hall, New York, 1941, pp. 463-6.

[7] Arndt and Eistert, *Ber.*, **69**, 2384 (1936).

[8] Hauser, *J. Am. Chem. Soc.*, **60**, 1957 (1938).

[9] Hauser and Renfrow, *J. Am. Chem. Soc.*, **59**, 1823 (1937).

[10] Snell and McElvain, *J. Am. Chem. Soc.*, **53**, 2310 (1931).

[11] Muller, Gawlick, and Kreutzmann, *Ann.*, **515**, 97 (1934).

[12] Schlenk, Hillemann, and Rodloff, *Ann.*, **487**, 135 (1931).

[13] Hauser and Renfrow, *Org. Syntheses*, **19**, 43 (1939), John Wiley & Sons, New York.

[14] Hudson and Hauser, *J. Am. Chem. Soc.*, **62**, 2457 (1940).

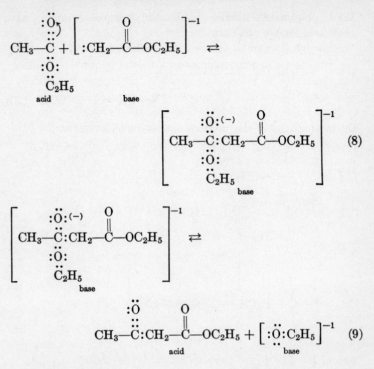

CONDENSATION WITH OTHER CARBONYL COMPOUNDS. *Carboxy Anhydrides* (Perkin reaction). Carboxy anhydrides, such as acetic acid anhydride, are usually condensed with aldehydes which do not contain active α-H atoms.[15] Although other aldehydes could be used, in this type of reaction, the formation of undesirable by-products restricts the choice of aldehydes. With an aldehyde containing no α-H atoms, the basic catalyst will react with the α-H atoms of the carboxy anhydride and produce a basic anion, as shown in equation 11.

The Perkin reaction, therefore, is fundamentally the reaction of an aldehyde (with no α-H atoms), an acid anhydride, and the sodium salt of its acid. After much controversy in regard to the function of the anhydride and its salt, it is now generally accepted that the anion of the salt serves the function of a basic catalyst.[16] Many other bases such as alkali metal acetates, carbonates, sul-

[15] Perkin, *J. Chem. Soc.*, **21**, 53, 181 (1868).
[16] Kalnin, *Helv. Chim. Acta*, **11**, 977 (1928).

fates, phosphates, pyridine, quinoline, and triethylamine have been used for the condensation.[17-19]

Although the overall reaction is represented as

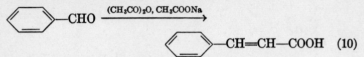

$$\text{(10)}$$

the mechanism [2] of the reaction can be shown as follows:

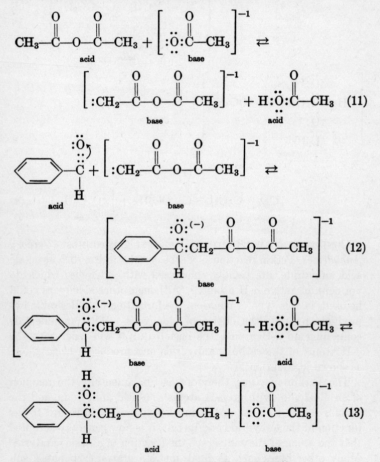

[17] Bakunin and Peccerillo, *Gazz. chim. ital.*, **65**, 1145 (1935).
[18] Kuhn and Ishikawa, *Ber.*, **64**, 2347 (1931).
[19] Muller, *Ann.*, **491**, 251 (1931).

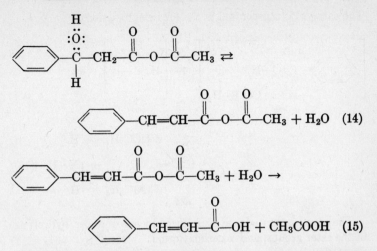

$$\text{—CH=CH—C—O—C—CH}_3 + \text{H}_2\text{O} \quad (14)$$

$$\text{—CH=CH—C—O—C—CH}_3 + \text{H}_2\text{O} \rightarrow$$

$$\text{—CH=CH—C—OH} + \text{CH}_3\text{COOH} \quad (15)$$

Malonic Ester Derivatives (Knoevenagel reaction). Malonic acid esters can be condensed with aldehydes through the use of a basic catalyst. The very labile α-H atom of the malonic ester reacts [2, 20] with the catalyst as follows:

$$
\begin{array}{ccccccc}
\text{COOC}_2\text{H}_5 & & \text{H} & & \left[\text{COOC}_2\text{H}_5\right]^{-1} & & \left[\begin{array}{c}\text{H}\end{array}\right]^{+1} \\
\text{H:C—H} & + & \text{:N—H} & \rightleftarrows & \text{:C—H} & + & \text{H:N—H} \\
\text{COOC}_2\text{H}_5 & & \text{H} & & \left[\text{COOC}_2\text{H}_5\right] & & \left[\text{H}\right]
\end{array}
\quad (16)
$$

acid   base   base   acid

The anion, thus formed, will undergo an acid-base reaction with the carbonyl compound:

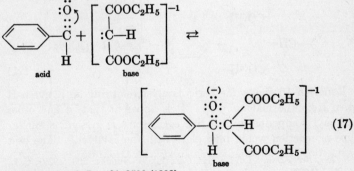

$$(17)$$

[20] Knoevenagel, *Ber.*, **31**, 2598 (1898).

The catalyst is regenerated in the following reaction:

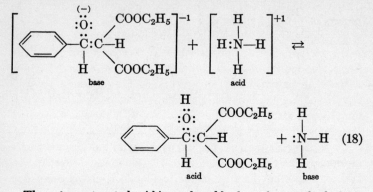

The α,β-unsaturated acid is produced by loss of water, hydrolysis of the ester groups, and decarboxylation:

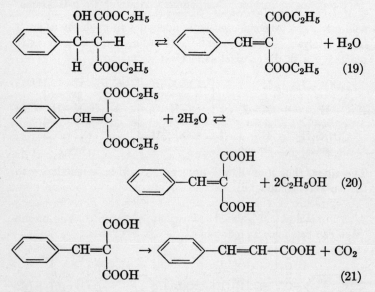

Equation 16 shows the basic catalyst removing an active α-H atom from the malonic ester. It is apparent that, if any other carbonyl compound with active α-H atoms is present, a similar type of reaction would take place with the catalyst.[21] The best

[21] Zaar, *Ber. Schimmel & Co. Akt. Ges.*, Jubilee Number, 299 (1929); *C.A.*, **24**, 2107 (1930).

results (fewer by-products) are obtained, therefore, when the malonic acid ester is condensed with carbonyl compounds containing no active α-H atoms.

The presence of two carbonyl groups in malonic ester makes the α-H atoms so reactive that it is possible to condense it with aldehydes, ketones, and esters containing only one carbonyl group, without getting too high a percentage of by-products.[22]   This reaction is feasible because in a competitive reaction of the carbonyl compounds containing α-H atom with the basic catalyst, the malonic ester having the most labile hydrogens will win out.

In the previously discussed Perkin reaction, limiting the choice of aldehyde to one containing no α-H atoms, i.e., benzaldehyde, is more important because of the less-labile H-atoms present in the aliphatic anhydrides.

3. Reactions of Carbonyl Compounds Containing No α-H Atoms.

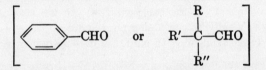

SELF-CONDENSATION. *Use of Electron-Release Catalyst* (Cannizzaro reaction). Fundamentally, the base-catalyzed Cannizzaro reaction involves the reaction between two molecules of an aldehyde containing no α-hydrogen atoms.[23]   The overall result is the transfer of one aldehyde hydrogen to another aldehyde group, thus producing two radicals that could combine to form an ester. The presence of the basic catalyst prevents the ester formation, and an alcohol and a metal carboxylate result.[24, 25]   The mechanism can be shown as follows:

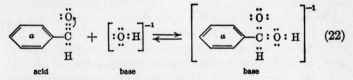

$$(22)$$

[22] von Auwers et al., *Ann.*, **432**, 46 (1923).
[23] Pomeranz, *Monatsh.*, **21**, 389 (1900).
[24] Euler and Lovgren, *Z. anorg. allgem. Chem.*, **147**, 123 (1925).
[25] Geib, *Z. physik. Chem.*, **A169**, 41 (1934).

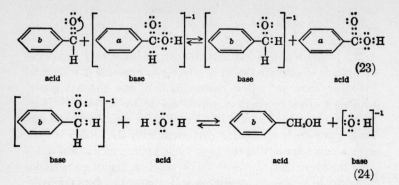

(23)

(24)

The amphoteric nature of benzaldehyde is shown by this base-catalyzed reaction and by the previously discussed (page 126) acid-catalyzed reaction to form an ester. In one reaction the carbonyl oxygen offers a share in an electron pair to the acid catalyst, and in the other reaction the carbonyl carbon accepts a share in an electron pair from the basic catalyst. In the base-catalyzed reactions of aldehydes containing no α-hydrogen the effect of the entering basic catalyst is to shift the carbon-hydrogen electron pair [6] toward the hydrogen, thus favoring $\overset{+}{C}$—$\overset{-}{H}$ rather than $\overset{-}{C}$—$\overset{+}{H}$ (equation 22). An electron shift in this direction is caused only with electron-release groups such as OH^{-1} and $OC_2H_5^{-1}$ ions. This change enables a hydride ion [2] to be split off more easily than it would be if the basic catalyst were an electron-withdrawal group, such as the cyanide ion. The latter group would cause the carbon-hydrogen electron pair to shift $\overset{-}{C}$—$\overset{+}{H}$ rather than $\overset{+}{C}$—$\overset{-}{H}$ and thus favor the removal of a proton rather than a hydride ion. Thus we can explain the specificity of the cyanide ion as a basic catalyst in the benzoin condensation, which will be discussed later.

The reaction in deuterium water [26] results in an alcohol containing no deuterium hydrogen attached to the carbon. Thus the transfer of a hydrogen from one aldehyde molecule to another does not involve water in the transfer mechanism.

Another example of the acidic behavior of the amphoteric aldehyde and the basic action of a catalyst in this type of reaction is the formation of benzyl benzoate under anhydrous conditions:

[26] Fredenhagen and Bonhoeffer, Z. physik. Chem., **A181**, 379 (1938).

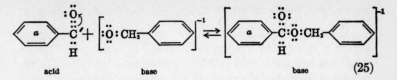

A second molecule of aldehyde reacts as an acid with this intermediate and removes a hydride ion, thus forming the neutral ester molecule and at the same time regenerating the basic catalyst, i.e., the benzylate ion:

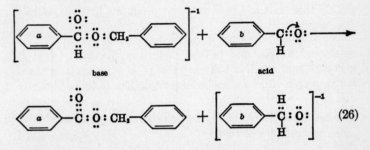

Use of the Electron-Withdrawal Catalyst (benzoin reaction).   The specificity of the basic cyanide ion used as a catalyst in the formation of benzoin has been considered puzzling, and apparently no adequate explanation has yet been suggested.[27]   Hydrogen cyanide, mercuric cyanide, and sodium hydroxide have no effect on the rate of benzoin formation, whereas sodium cyanide, potassium cyanide, and barium cyanide have a powerful catalytic effect.[28]

The kinetics of the reaction, however, leaves little doubt that the following mechanism [27] exists:

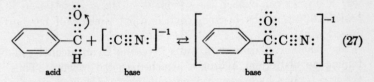

In the product formed, the cyanide group, which is an electron-withdrawal group, greatly activates the α-hydrogen by causing

[27] Hammett, *Physical Organic Chemistry*, McGraw-Hill Book Company, New York, 1940, p. 349.

[28] Lapworth, *J. Chem. Soc.*, **83**, 995 (1903).

an electron displacement in the C—H bond which results in $\overset{-}{C}$—$\overset{+}{H}$ rather than $\overset{+}{C}$—$\overset{-}{H}$. Therefore, instead of a hydride ion, a proton is split off by the oxygen of a similar molecule. The net result can be considered a shift of a proton from the carbon to the oxygen of the carbonyl group. It seems reasonable to suspect that the specificity of the cyanide ion as a catalyst for this reaction is due to the fact that it has electron-withdrawal properties. The other common basic catalysts, such as OH^{-1}, $OC_2H_5^{-1}$, and the amines, all have electron-release properties, which would cause the electron shift to $\overset{+}{C}$—$\overset{-}{H}$ and thus produce a hydride ion rather than a proton:

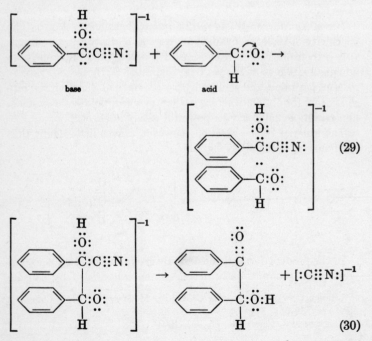

$$\rightleftharpoons \tag{28}$$

A second molecule of the benzaldehyde reacts as an acid with this basic complex as follows:

base   acid

$$\tag{29}$$

$$+ [:C::N:]^{-1} \tag{30}$$

CONDENSATION WITH OTHER CARBONYL COMPOUNDS. The condensation of aldehydes having no α-H atoms with other carbonyl compounds has already been discussed. The Perkin and Knoevenagel reactions fall in this catagory.

In discussing the above reactions, we emphasized the effect of the basic catalyst on the α-H atoms of the carbonyl compounds (i.e., carboxy anhydrides and malonic esters). The resulting anions accelerated the formation of the end products of these reactions. The anions were shown to react with an aldehyde containing no α-H atoms (equations 12 and 17).

It is obvious, from the reactions already discussed, that the basic catalyst will have practically no effect on carbonyl compounds having no α-H atoms, if other carbonyl compounds containing α-H atoms are present.

4. Summary.

In all the examples of basic catalysis considered above, the characteristic effect of the basic catalyst is the increase in concentration of the basic group involved in the reaction. This is accomplished by the familiar displacement of one base by another: for example, the displacement of the ester anion from ethyl acetate by the ethoxide ion catalyst in the Claisen reaction. In some reactions, however, displacement apparently does not result, but the combination of the basic catalyst with the reacting substance merely localizes the electron excess on one atom, which can then act as a base. An example is the shifting of the electron pair of the C—H linkage toward the hydrogen in the base-catalyzed Cannizzaro reaction, thus enabling a second molecule of aldehyde to remove a hydride ion.

Chapter 12

ALKOXIDES AS CATALYSTS

1. Introduction.

The importance and widespread use of many alkoxides as catalysts warrants a brief discussion of the role they play in reaction mechanisms. These catalysts may often lead to "surprising" results if the acidic, basic, or amphoteric nature of the alkoxide is not considered.

The alkoxides may be amphoteric, highly acidic, or highly basic. Alkali metal alkoxides such as sodium ethoxide are basic in reactions because of the ethoxide [1-3] ion $(OC_2H_5^{-1})$. Aluminum alkoxide,[4] $Al(OR)_3$, would be primarily acidic in behavior because of the strong tendency of the electrophilic (i.e., acidic) aluminum atom to accept a share in a pair of electrons from an electrodotic compound (i.e., a base). Toward another, stronger acid, however, aluminum alkoxide would react as a base as does aluminum hydroxide. A survey of the literature shows several very interesting investigations in the field of catalytic condensations of aldehydes in which acidic, basic, and amphoteric catalysts are used. Kulpinski and Nord [5] have reported the use of an alkoxide ("complex"), $Mg[Al(OR)_4]_2$, which, according to their experimental results, seems to exhibit amphoteric behavior.

With these facts clarified by the application of the electronic theory of acids and bases, a much better understanding of aldehyde reactions seems possible.

[1] Hauser, *J. Am. Chem. Soc.*, **60**, 1957 (1938).

[2] Hauser and Renfrow, *J. Am. Chem. Soc.*, **59**, 1823 (1937).

[3] Snell and McElvain, *J. Am. Chem. Soc.*, **53**, 2310 (1931).

[4] Tischtschenko, *Chem. Zentr.*, **77**, 1309, 1552 (1906).

[5] Kulpinski and Nord, *J. Org. Chem.*, **8**, 256 (1943).

2. Basic Alkoxide Catalysts.

Aldehydes having a —CH$_2$— group in the alpha position (such as propanal) will behave as acids in the presence of a strongly basic catalyst like OH^{-1} or OC$_2$H$_5^{-1}$ ions.[6] Thus, NaOC$_2$H$_5$ would react with an aldehyde as follows:

$$R-\overset{\overset{\text{H}}{|}}{\underset{\underset{\text{H}}{|}}{\overset{..}{\underset{..}{C}}}}-\overset{\overset{\text{O}}{\|}}{\underset{\underset{\text{H}}{|}}{C}} + \left[:\overset{..}{\underset{..}{O}}:C_2H_5\right]^{-1} \rightleftarrows \left[R-\overset{\overset{\text{H}}{|}}{\underset{\underset{\text{H}}{|}}{\overset{..}{\underset{..}{C}}}}-\overset{\overset{\text{O}}{\|}}{C}\right]^{-1} + H:\overset{..}{\underset{..}{O}}:C_2H_5 \quad (1)$$

acid   base   base

The actual mechanism that results in this proton removal by the basic catalyst is not particularly important. It may be a coordination of the base with the proton accompanied by an ionization, or a coordination of the basic catalyst with the carbonyl carbon followed by an α,γ-shift. In either mechanism the catalytic effect is due to the increase in concentration of the carbanion that results from this first step.

This type of reaction leads to an aldolization (formation of a compound similar to aldol)

$$R'-CH_2-\overset{\overset{..}{\overset{:O}{\vdots}}}{\underset{\underset{\text{H}}{|}}{C}}+ \left[\overset{\overset{\text{H}}{|}}{\underset{\underset{\text{R}}{|}}{:C}}-\overset{\overset{\text{O}}{\|}}{\underset{\underset{\text{H}}{|}}{C}}\right]^{-1} \rightleftarrows \left[R'-CH_2-\overset{\overset{:\overset{..}{O}:}{|}}{\underset{\underset{\text{H}}{|}}{\overset{..}{C}}}:\overset{\overset{\text{H}}{|}}{\underset{\underset{\text{R}}{|}}{C}}-\overset{\overset{\text{O}}{\|}}{\underset{\underset{\text{H}}{|}}{C}}\right]^{-1} \quad (2)$$

acid   base   base

or, if a molecule of water is subsequently eliminated on acidification, crotonization (formation of a compound similar to croton-aldehyde) will result:

$$\left[R'-CH_2-\overset{\overset{:\overset{..}{O}:}{|}}{\underset{\underset{\text{H}}{|}}{\overset{..}{C}}}-\overset{\overset{\text{H}}{|}}{\underset{\underset{\text{R}}{|}}{C}}-\overset{\overset{\text{O}}{\|}}{\underset{\underset{\text{H}}{|}}{C}}\right]^{-1} \overset{H^{+1}}{\underset{}{\rightleftarrows}} R'-CH_2-\overset{\overset{:\overset{..}{O}:\text{H}}{|}}{\underset{\underset{\text{H}}{|}}{\overset{..}{C}}}-\overset{\overset{\text{H}}{|}}{\underset{\underset{\text{R}}{|}}{C}}-\overset{\overset{\text{O}}{\|}}{\underset{\underset{\text{H}}{|}}{C}} \overset{-H_2O}{\rightleftarrows}$$

base

$$R'-CH_2-\overset{}{\underset{\underset{\text{H}}{|}}{C}}=\overset{}{\underset{\underset{\text{R}}{|}}{C}}-\overset{\overset{\text{O}}{\|}}{\underset{\underset{\text{H}}{|}}{C}} \quad (3)$$

[6] Bell, *J. Chem. Soc.*, **1937**, 1637.

Aldehydes that have available only one hydrogen in the alpha position, such as the α-alkyl aldehydes (—CHR—CHO), are less acidic [7] than those containing a —CH$_2$— group in the alpha position. This is due to the electron-release effect of the alkyl group which displaces the C—H electron pair nearer to the proton and makes the proton removal by the basic catalyst more difficult. Aldolization of such aldehydes would, therefore, require strongly basic catalysts.

It is apparent from this discussion that alkali metal alkoxides, such as NaOC$_2$H$_5$, which furnish a high concentration of OC$_2$H$_5$$^{-1}$ ions, will behave as strongly basic (electrodotic) catalysts. Their use with aldehydes would produce an aldolization or crotonization if active α-hydrogens are available. Therefore, the experimental observation [5] that alpha —CH$_2$— and —CHR— aldehydes behave similarly toward alkali metal alkoxides is to be expected, since these strongly basic catalysts will cause both types of aldehydes to behave as acids to produce similar types of compounds.

When no α-hydrogen is available in the aldehyde (such as benzaldehyde), a stronger base, like OH^{-1}, is needed to catalyze the reaction by coordinating with the carbonyl carbon:

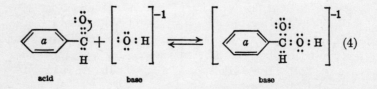

$$\text{(4)}$$

This coordination leads to a Cannizzaro type of reaction (see Chapter 11). The effect of the coordinated OH^{-1} group is to displace the C—H electron pair nearer to the hydrogen $\overset{+}{C}$—$\overset{-}{H}$ so that a hydride ion may be split off by another aldehyde group acting as an acid:

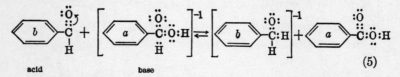

$$\text{(5)}$$

[7] Gilman, *Organic Chemistry*, John Wiley & Sons, New York, 1943, Vol. II, p. 1844.

Benzyl alcohol and sodium benzoate are formed in the presence of sodium hydroxide. This change has often been referred to as an oxidation-reduction reaction, but experimental evidence has shown that oxidizing agents have no catalytic effect.[8] This result would support the conclusion that the reaction is of the generalized acid-base type.

3. Acidic Alkoxide Catalysts.

The amphoteric nature of carbonyl compounds is shown by the fact that their reactions can be catalyzed by acids as well as bases. In the preceding section it has been shown that aldehydes behave as acids in the presence of alkali metal alkoxides.

The basic behavior of carbonyl compounds such as aldehydes is illustrated by their condensation reactions in the presence of aluminum alkoxides (acids).

Alkoxides like $Al(OR)_3$ will behave as fairly strong acid catalysts,[1-3] owing to the tendency of the aluminum atom in these compounds to accept a share in a pair of electrons. In view of this fact it is to be expected that aluminum alkoxides will cause the amphoteric aldehydes to behave as bases, so that a simple ester results. As this behavior involves only the basic characteristics of the carbonyl group itself it makes little difference whether we have one, two, or no α-hydrogen atoms in the aldehyde; an ester is the result.[4] The first step is a typical acid-base neutralization reaction with the formation of a coordinate covalent bond:

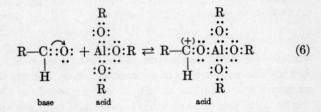

$$(6)$$

The acidic (electrophilic) aluminum atom makes the carbonyl carbon so positive that it can remove a hydride ion [8] from another aldehyde molecule:

[8] Hammett, *Physical Organic Chemistry*, McGraw-Hill Book Company, New York, 1940, p. 350.

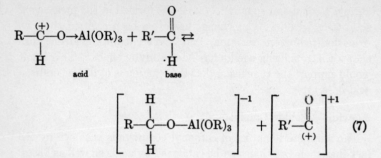

(7)

Thus a simple ester is formed:

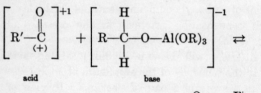

$$R'-\overset{\overset{\textstyle O}{\|}}{C}-O-\overset{\overset{\textstyle H}{|}}{\underset{\underset{\textstyle H}{|}}{C}}-R + Al(OR)_3 \quad (8)$$

4. "Complex" Alkoxide Catalysts.

Kulpinski and Nord [5] describe the use of "complex" alkoxide catalysts for the condensation of aldehydes to glycol esters. These catalysts are of a type represented by $Mg[Al(OR)_4]_2$, a substance that evidently consists of Mg^{+2} ions and $Al(OR)_4^{-1}$ ions. With aldehydes having $-CH_2-$ in the alpha position, this catalyst produces mainly glycol esters. However, with aldehydes having $-CHR-$ in the alpha position, mainly simple esters are formed. Although these reactions may seem puzzling at first, they are readily understood when the amphoteric nature of the aldehydes and the catalysts is taken into consideration, from the viewpoint of the electronic theory of acids and bases.

These "complex" catalysts can react as weak acids (because of Mg^{+2}) or as weak bases (because of $Al(OR)_4^{-1}$). The manner in which the catalyst reacts depends on the relative acidity or basicity of the aldehyde involved.

The aldehydes having $-CH_2-$ in the alpha position are more acidic than the aldehydes having $-CHR-$ in the alpha position.[7]

Apparently the former behave as acids toward the $Al(OR)_4^{-1}$ part of the catalyst, because aldolization is the result:

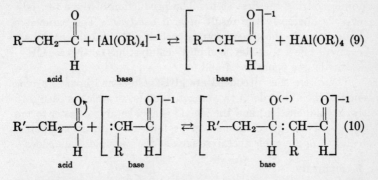

$$(9)$$

The aldol-type compounds formed in such reactions are really aldehydes having —CHR— groups in the alpha position (except acetaldehyde).[9] These aldehydes are more basic than the aldehydes containing a —CH₂— group in the alpha position, and therefore the acidic Mg^{+2} ion rather than the basic $Al(OR)_4^{-1}$ might be expected to acid-catalyze the reaction in the typical way to produce an ester (glycol ester):

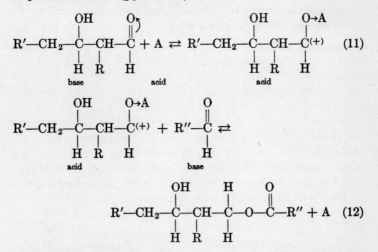

[9] Kulpinski and Nord (see note 5) report a very low yield of glycol ester with acetaldehyde. This is probably due to the fact that no alpha-alkyl aldehyde is produced here, and, therefore, practically no acidic catalysis follows the aldolization to produce an ester.

Whether the catalyst is Mg^{+2} is questionable in view of the presence of $HAl(OR)_4$, another and probably stronger acid [10] formed during the first step. The production of the ester, however, is obviously the result of acid catalysis. The removal of hydride ion in the second step is probably facilitated by the basic catalytic effect that the "complex" catalyst has on this α—CH_2—aldehyde (see equations 4 and 5).

The esters thus produced are glycol esters and involve a reaction of the aldehyde in two stages, the first of which is base-catalyzed (aldolization) and the second is acid catalyzed (ester formation). These glycol esters will be formed [5] with an amphoteric catalyst or a complex catalyst such as the "complex" alkoxides.

5. Summary.

An understanding of the electronic theory of acids and bases is of great assistance in the interpretation of catalytic condensations of aldehydes. The reactions are easily explained when the acid-base characteristics of both the aldehydes and the catalysts are understood.

Strongly basic alkoxide catalysts result in aldolization (and crotonization) only; acidic alkoxides produce simple esters only. Amphoteric or "complex" alkoxides, however, may combine both reactions and produce a glycol ester.

[10] Meerwein, *Ann.*, **455**, 227 (1927).

Chapter 13

CONCLUSION

In the Preface we postponed a more detailed discussion of the real function of the electronic theory of acids and bases in chemistry until now. More discussion of the theory itself was necessary before its significance could be presented.

As first proposed by Lewis, the electronic theory of acids and bases was not directly related to the phenomena of oxidation and reduction. But we have tried to bring out the relationship between these two aspects of chemical behavior and to place them both in a larger setting. Both are manifestations of the relative attraction of two chemical substances for electrons.

The electrophilic nature of a chemical substance is not an absolute property like its density. Its action as an electrophile is relative to any number of other substances. If it is reacting with a base it gains only a share in a pair of electrons; if it is reacting with a reducing agent it gains electrons outright. Furthermore, the same substance may also behave as an electrodote toward another set of substances, i.e., as a base toward stronger acids and as a reducing agent toward oxidizing agents.

At first this relativity may seem a bit disconcerting. But it is a part of the experimental facts, however we interpret them. We have only to remember water as an example (as discussed in Chapter 4) to see how true this is. The water molecule by itself is neither electrophile (acid or oxidant) nor electrodote (base or reductant). But it behaves as an acid toward ammonia, as an oxidant toward sodium, as a base toward sulfur dioxide, as a reductant toward fluorine. All these words—acid, oxidant, base, reductant—describe the behavior of water toward other substances. This behavior does not depend upon any particular element, but upon the relative attraction of the different pairs of substances for electrons. The result is most simply expressed as the achievement of a more stable arrangement of electrons.

This more stable overall arrangement of electrons can be achieved in three ways: (1) outright transfer of electrons (oxidation-reduction); (2) formation of new coordinate covalent bonds (acid-base phenomena); (3) formation of covalent bonds (odd-electron-molecule reactions). The second of the three is the only one needing any further discussion here. New coordinate covalent bonds may be formed in two ways: (a) neutralization as discussed in Chapters 3 and 6, and (b) displacement as presented in Chapter 8 and in the chapters on catalysis. A more stable overall arrangement of electrons in the molecules concerned is brought about by either reaction.

The one unifying principle underlying all chemistry is simply this: those reactions occur which lead to the formation of molecules having the most stable electron configuration.

We now see more clearly the function of the Lewis theory of acids and bases. The elimination of the idea that acidity depends upon the presence of a particular element permits a much greater systematization of chemical reactions than has been possible in the past.

Much remains to be done in the way of quantitative measurement as suggested by this new relativity in chemistry. No doubt, as more and more experimental results accumulate, the theory will undergo modification and refinement. Eventually it may give way entirely to another, but the least that can be said for it now is that it can rid chemistry forever of one-element theories of the behavior of matter. This in itself is an accomplishment of considerable magnitude. It opens up our minds as widely as any previous idea in chemistry has ever done.

INDEX

Acceptor molecules, 16
Acetate ion, 7, 8
Acetates, basic behavior of, 138
Acetic acid, 8, 9, 47, 56
  association of, 40
  titration of, 92
Acetone, as a base, 16
  displaced by pyridine, 99
Acid, 43
Acid-analogous, 13
Acidic radicals, 62, 63
Activation, 60, 62
Acylation, mechanism of, 123
  with carboxy anhydrides, 125
  with carboxy compounds, 124
  with esters, 123
Addition compounds, 88
Alcohols, basic behavior of, 109, 117
  halogenation of, 129
  titration of, 92, 93
Aldehydes, acidic behavior of, 112
  amphoteric behavior of, 61
  basic behavior of, 126, 127
  reaction with semicarbazide, 127
Aldol condensations, 138, 151
Alkali metal acetates, catalytic action
  of, 141
Alkoxides, alkali metal, 151
  aluminum, 50
  basic behavior of, 111
  catalytic effect of, 111, 126, 140
Alkyl halides, alkylation with, 115
  basic behavior of, 115
Alkylation, mechanism of, 110, 116,
  119
  with alcohols, 109, 117
  with alkyl halides, 115
  with allyl alcohol, 122
  with benzyl chloride, 121
  with cinnamic acid, 122
  with esters, 120

Alkylation, with ethers, 119
  with olefins, 111, 116
  with 3-phenyl-1-propene, 122
Allyl alcohol, alkylation with, 122
Aluminum alkoxides, acidic behavior
  of, 50, 126, 153
  catalytic effect of, 126
Aluminum amide, 56
Aluminum bromide, 43, 44
Aluminum chloride, 10, 11, 12, 16, 19,
  20, 45
  catalytic effect of, 110, 115, 117, 124
  titration of, 93
Aluminum hydroxide, 11, 56, 60
Aluminum sulfite, 11
Amide ion, 9, 55
Amino radicals, 81, 83
Ammonia, as a base, 6, 7, 9, 17, 39, 41,
  42, 43
  displaced by triethylamine, 99
  solvent, 10, 56
  titration of, 92
Ammonium chloride, 60
Ammonium iodide, 10
Ammonium ion, 6, 7, 8, 9, 41
  as an oxidizing agent, 10
Ammonium sulfide, 14
Ammono acid, 10
Amphoteric behavior, 60, 61, 71
Amphoteric behavior of, aluminum
  amide, 56
  aluminum hydroxide, 56
  benzaldehyde, 146
  hydrogen chloride, 74
  iodide ion, 65
  quinhydrone, 75
  quinone, 75
  water, 74, 75
  zinc acetate, 56
  zinc amide, 10, 56
  zinc hydroxide, 10, 56

159

CATALOG OF DOVER BOOKS

BOOKS EXPLAINING SCIENCE AND MATHEMATICS

THE COMMON SENSE OF THE EXACT SCIENCES, W. K. Clifford. Introduction by James Newman, edited by Karl Pearson. For 70 years this has been a guide to classical scientific and mathematical thought. Explains with unusual clarity basic concepts, such as extension of meaning of symbols, characteristics of surface boundaries, properties of plane figures, vectors, Cartesian method of determining position, etc. Long preface by Bertrand Russell. Bibliography of Clifford. Corrected, 130 diagrams redrawn. 249pp. 5⅜ x 8.
T61 Paperbound **$1.60**

SCIENCE THEORY AND MAN, Erwin Schrödinger. This is a complete and unabridged reissue of SCIENCE AND THE HUMAN TEMPERAMENT plus an additional essay: "What is an Elementary Particle?" Nobel Laureate Schrödinger discusses such topics as nature of scientific method, the nature of science, chance and determinism, science and society, conceptual models for physical entities, elementary particles and wave mechanics. Presentation is popular and may be followed by most people with little or no scientific training. "Fine practical preparation for a time when laws of nature, human institutions . . . are undergoing a critical examination without parallel," Waldemar Kaempffert, N. Y. TIMES. 192pp. 5⅜ x 8.
T428 Paperbound **$1.35**

PIONEERS OF SCIENCE, O. Lodge. Eminent scientist-expositor's authoritative, yet elementary survey of great scientific theories. Concentrating on individuals—Copernicus, Brahe, Kepler, Galileo, Descartes, Newton, Laplace, Herschel, Lord Kelvin, and other scientists—the author presents their discoveries in historical order adding biographical material on each man and full, specific explanations of their achievements. The clear and complete treatment of the post-Newtonian astronomers is a feature seldom found in other books on the subject. Index. 120 illustrations. xv + 404pp. 5⅜ x 8.
T716 Paperbound **$1.50**

THE EVOLUTION OF SCIENTIFIC THOUGHT FROM NEWTON TO EINSTEIN, A. d'Abro. Einstein's special and general theories of relativity, with their historical implications, are analyzed in non-technical terms. Excellent accounts of the contributions of Newton, Riemann, Weyl, Planck, Eddington, Maxwell, Lorentz and others are treated in terms of space and time, equations of electromagnetics, finiteness of the universe, methodology of science. 21 diagrams. 482pp. 5⅜ x 8.
T2 Paperound **$2.00**

THE RISE OF THE NEW PHYSICS, A. d'Abro. A half-million word exposition, formerly titled THE DECLINE OF MECHANISM, for readers not versed in higher mathematics. The only thorough explanation, in everyday language, of the central core of modern mathematical physical theory, treating both classical and modern theoretical physics, and presenting in terms almost anyone can understand the equivalent of 5 years of study of mathematical physics. Scientifically impeccable coverage of mathematical-physical thought from the Newtonian system up through the electronic theories of Dirac and Heisenberg and Fermi's statistics. Combines both history and exposition; provides a broad yet unified and detailed view, with constant comparison of classical and modern views on phenomena and theories. "A must for anyone doing serious study in the physical sciences," JOURNAL OF THE FRANKLIN INSTITUTE. "Extraordinary faculty . . . to explain ideas and theories of theoretical physics in the language of daily life," ISIS. First part of set covers philosophy of science, drawing upon the practice of Newton, Maxwell, Poincaré, Einstein, others, discussing modes of thought, experiment, interpretations of causality, etc. In the second part, 100 pages explain grammar and vocabulary of mathematics, with discussions of functions, groups, series, Fourier series, etc. The remainder is devoted to concrete, detailed coverage of both classical and quantum physics, explaining such topics as analytic mechanics, Hamilton's principle, wave theory of light, electromagnetic waves, groups of transformations, thermodynamics, phase rule, Brownian movement, kinetics, special relativity, Planck's original quantum theory, Bohr's atom, Zeeman effect, Broglie's wave mechanics, Heisenberg's uncertainty, Eigen-values, matrices, scores of other important topics. Discoveries and theories are covered for such men as Alembert, Born, Cantor, Debye, Euler, Foucault, Galois, Gauss, Hadamard, Kelvin, Kepler, Laplace, Maxwell, Pauli, Rayleigh, Volterra, Weyl, Young, more than 180 others. Indexed. 97 illustrations. ix + 982pp. 5⅜ x 8.
T3 Volume 1, Paperbound **$2.00**
T4 Volume 2, Paperbound **$2.00**

CONCERNING THE NATURE OF THINGS, Sir William Bragg. Christmas lectures delivered at the Royal Society by Nobel laureate. Why a spinning ball travels in a curved track; how uranium is transmuted to lead, etc. Partial contents: atoms, gases, liquids, crystals, metals, etc. No scientific background needed; wonderful for intelligent child. 32pp. of photos, 57 figures. xii + 232pp. 5⅜ x 8.
T31 Paperbound **$1.35**

THE UNIVERSE OF LIGHT, Sir William Bragg. No scientific training needed to read Nobel Prize winner's expansion of his Royal Institute Christmas Lectures. Insight into nature of light, methods and philosophy of science. Explains lenses, reflection, color, resonance, polarization, x-rays, the spectrum, Newton's work with prisms, Huygens' with polarization, Crookes' with cathode ray, etc. Leads into clear statement of 2 major historical theories of light, corpuscle and wave. Dozens of experiments you can do. 199 illus., including 2 full-page color plates. 293pp. 5⅜ x 8.
S538 Paperbound **$1.85**

PHYSICS, THE PIONEER SCIENCE, L. W. Taylor. First thorough text to place all important physical phenomena in cultural-historical framework; remains best work of its kind. Exposition of physical laws, theories developed chronologically, with great historical, illustrative experiments diagrammed, described, worked out mathematically. Excellent physics text for self-study as well as class work. Vol. 1: Heat, Sound: motion, acceleration, gravitation, conservation of energy, heat engines, rotation, heat, mechanical energy, etc. 211 illus. 407pp. 5⅜ x 8. Vol. 2: Light, Electricity: images, lenses, prisms, magnetism, Ohm's law, dynamos, telegraph, quantum theory, decline of mechanical view of nature, etc. Bibliography. 13 table appendix. Index. 551 illus. 2 color plates. 508pp. 5⅜ x 8.

Vol. 1 S565 Paperbound **$2.00**
Vol. 2 S566 Paperbound **$2.00**
The set **$4.00**

FROM EUCLID TO EDDINGTON: A STUDY OF THE CONCEPTIONS OF THE EXTERNAL WORLD, Sir Edmund Whittaker. A foremost British scientist traces the development of theories of natural philosophy from the western rediscovery of Euclid to Eddington, Einstein, Dirac, etc. The inadequacy of classical physics is contrasted with present day attempts to understand the physical world through relativity, non-Euclidean geometry, space curvature, wave mechanics, etc. 5 major divisions of examination: Space; Time and Movement; the Concepts of Classical Physics; the Concepts of Quantum Mechanics; the Eddington Universe. 212pp. 5⅜ x 8.
T491 Paperbound **$1.35**

THE STORY OF ATOMIC THEORY AND ATOMIC ENERGY, J. G. Feinberg. Wider range of facts on physical theory, cultural implications, than any other similar source. Completely non-technical. Begins with first atomic theory, 600 B.C., goes through A-bomb, developments to 1959. Avogadro, Rutherford, Bohr, Einstein, radioactive decay, binding energy, radiation danger, future benefits of nuclear power, dozens of other topics, told in lively, related, informal manner. Particular stress on European atomic research. "Deserves special mention . . . authoritative," Saturday Review. Formerly "The Atom Story." New chapter to 1959. Index. 34 illustrations. 251pp. 5⅜ x 8.
T625 Paperbound **$1.45**

THE STRANGE STORY OF THE QUANTUM, AN ACCOUNT FOR THE GENERAL READER OF THE GROWTH OF IDEAS UNDERLYING OUR PRESENT ATOMIC KNOWLEDGE, B. Hoffmann. Presents lucidly and expertly, with barest amount of mathematics, the problems and theories which led to modern quantum physics. Dr. Hoffmann begins with the closing years of the 19th century, when certain trifling discrepancies were noticed, and with illuminating analogies and examples takes you through the brilliant concepts of Planck, Einstein, Pauli, de Broglie, Bohr, Schroedinger, Heisenberg, Dirac, Sommerfeld, Feynman, etc. This edition includes a new, long postscript carrying the story through 1958. "Of the books attempting an account of the history and contents of our modern atomic physics which have come to my attention, this is the best," H. Margenau, Yale University, in "American Journal of Physics." 32 tables and line illustrations. Index. 275pp. 5⅜ x 8.
T518 Paperbound **$1.45**

SPACE AND TIME, Emile Borel. An entirely non-technical introduction to relativity, by world-renowned mathematician, Sorbonne Professor. (Notes on basic mathematics are included separately.) This book has never been surpassed for insight, and extraordinary clarity of thought, as it presents scores of examples, analogies, arguments, illustrations, which explain such topics as: difficulties due to motion; gravitation a force of inertia; geodesic lines; wave-length and difference of phase; x-rays and crystal structure; the special theory of relativity; and much more. Indexes. 4 appendixes. 15 figures. xvi + 243pp. 5⅜ x 8.
T592 Paperbound **$1.45**

THE RESTLESS UNIVERSE, Max Born. New enlarged version of this remarkably readable account by a Nobel laureate. Moving from sub-atomic particles to universe, the author explains in very simple terms the latest theories of wave mechanics. Partial contents: air and its relatives, electrons & ions, waves & particles, electronic structure of the atom, nuclear physics. Nearly 1000 illustrations, including 7 animated sequences. 325pp. 6 x 9.
T412 Paperbound **$2.00**

SOAP SUBBLES, THEIR COLOURS AND THE FORCES WHICH MOULD THEM, C. V. Boys. Only complete edition, half again as much material as any other. Includes Boys' hints on performing his experiments, sources of supply. Dozens of lucid experiments show complexities of liquid films, surface tension, etc. Best treatment ever written. Introduction. 83 illustrations. Color plate. 202pp. 5⅜ x 8.
T542 Paperbound **95¢**

SPINNING TOPS AND GYROSCOPIC MOTION, John Perry. Well-known classic of science still unsurpassed for lucid, accurate, delightful exposition. How quasi-rigidity is induced in flexible and fluid bodies by rapid motions; why gyrostat falls, top rises; nature and effect on climatic conditions of earth's precessional movement; effect of internal fluidity on rotating bodies, etc. Appendixes describe practical uses to which gyroscopes have been put in ships, compasses, monorail transportation. 62 figures. 128pp. 5⅜ x 8.
T416 Paperbound **$1.00**

MATTER & LIGHT, THE NEW PHYSICS, L. de Broglie. Non-technical papers by a Nobel laureate explain electromagnetic theory, relativity, matter, light and radiation, wave mechanics, quantum physics, philosophy of science. Einstein, Planck, Bohr, others explained so easily that no mathematical training is needed for all but 2 of the 21 chapters. Unabridged. Index. 300pp. 5⅜ x 8.
T35 Paperbound **$1.60**

A SURVEY OF PHYSICAL THEORY, Max Planck. One of the greatest scientists of all time, creator of the quantum revolution in physics, writes in non-technical terms of his own discoveries and those of other outstanding creators of modern physics. Planck wrote this book when science had just crossed the threshold of the new physics, and he communicates the excitement felt then as he discusses electromagnetic theories, statistical methods, evolution of the concept of light, a step-by-step description of how he developed his own momentous theory, and many more of the basic ideas behind modern physics. Formerly "A" Survey of Physics." Bibliography. Index. 128pp. 5⅜ x 8.　　　　　　　　　S650 Paperbound **$1.15**

THE NATURE OF LIGHT AND COLOUR IN THE OPEN AIR, M. Minnaert. Why is falling snow sometimes black? What causes mirages, the fata morgana, multiple suns and moons in the sky? How are shadows formed? Prof. Minnaert of the University of Utrecht answers these and similar questions in optics, light, colour, for non-specialists. Particularly valuable to nature, science students, painters, photographers. Translated by H. M. Kremer-Priest, K. Jay. 202 illustrations, including 42 photos. xvi + 362pp. 5⅜ x 8.　　　　　T196 Paperbound **$1.95**

THE STORY OF X-RAYS FROM RONTGEN TO ISOTOPES, A. R. Bleich. Non-technical history of x-rays, their scientific explanation, their applications in medicine, industry, research, and art, and their effect on the individual and his descendants. Includes amusing early reactions to Röntgen's discovery, cancer therapy, detections of art and stamp forgeries, potential risks to patient and operator, etc. Illustrations show x-rays of flower structure, the gall bladder, gears with hidden defects, etc. Original Dover publication. Glossary. Bibliography. Index. 55 photos and figures. xiv + 186pp. 5⅜ x 8.　　　　　T662 Paperbound **$1.35**

TEACH YOURSELF ELECTRICITY, C. W. Wilman. Electrical resistance, inductance, capacitance, magnets, chemical effects of current, alternating currents, generators and motors, transformers, rectifiers, much more. 230 questions, answers, worked examples. List of units. 115 illus. 194pp. 6⅞ x 4¼.　　　　　　　　　　　　　　　　　　Clothbound **$2.00**

TEACH YOURSELF HEAT ENGINES, E. De Ville. Measurement of heat, development of steam and internal combustion engines, efficiency of an engine, compression-ignition engines, production of steam, the ideal engine, much more. 318 exercises, answers, worked examples. Tables. 76 illus. 220pp. 6⅞ x 4¼.　　　　　　　　　　　　　　　　　　Clothbound **$2.00**

TEACH YOURSELF MECHANICS, P. Abbott. The lever, centre of gravity, parallelogram of force, friction, acceleration, Newton's laws of motion, machines, specific gravity, gas, liquid pressure, much more. 280 problems, solutions. Tables. 163 illus. 271pp. 6⅞ x 4¼.　　　　　　　　　　　　　　　　　　　　　　　　　　Clothbound **$2.00**

GREAT IDEAS OF MODERN MATHEMATICS: THEIR NATURE AND USE, Jagjit Singh. Reader with only high school math will understand main mathematical ideas of modern physics, astronomy, genetics, psychology, evolution, etc., better than many who use them as tools, but comprehend little of their basic structure. Author uses his wide knowledge of non-mathematical fields in brilliant exposition of differential equations, matrices, group theory, logic, statistics, problems of mathematical foundations, imaginary numbers, vectors, etc. Original publication. 2 appendixes. 2 indexes. 65 illustr. 322pp. 5⅜ x 8.　　　　S587 Paperbound **$1.55**

MATHEMATICS IN ACTION, O. G. Sutton. Everyone with a command of high school algebra will find this book one of the finest possible introductions to the application of mathematics to physical theory. Ballistics, numerical analysis, waves and wavelike phenomena, Fourier series, group concepts, fluid flow and aerodynamics, statistical measures, and meteorology are discussed with unusual clarity. Some calculus and differential equations theory is developed by the author for the reader's help in the more difficult sections. 88 figures. Index. viii + 236pp. 5⅜ x 8.　　　　　　　　　　　　　T440 Clothbound **$3.50**

FREE! All you do is ask for it!

A DOVER SCIENCE SAMPLER, edited by George Barkin. 64-page book, sturdily bound, containing excerpts from over 20 Dover books explaining science. Edwin Hubble, George Sarton, Ernst Mach, A. d'Abro, Galileo, Newton, others, discussing island universes, scientific truth, biological phenomena, stability in bridges, etc. Copies limited, no more than 1 to a customer.　　　FREE

THE FOURTH DIMENSION SIMPLY EXPLAINED, edited by H. P. Manning. 22 essays, originally Scientific American contest entries, that use a minimum of mathematics to explain aspects of 4-dimensional geometry: analogues to 3-dimensional space, 4-dimensional absurdities and curiosities (such as removing the contents of an egg without puncturing its shell), possible measurements and forms, etc. Introduction by the editor. Only book of its sort on a truly elementary level, excellent introduction to advanced works. 82 figures. 251pp. 5⅜ x 8.　　　　　　　　　　　　　　　　　　　　　　　　T711 Paperbound **$1.35**

FAMOUS BRIDGES OF THE WORLD, D. B. Steinman. An up-to-the-minute revised edition of a book that explains the fascinating drama of how the world's great bridges came to be built. The author, designer of the famed Mackinac bridge, discusses bridges from all periods and all parts of the world, explaining their various types of construction, and describing the problems their builders faced. Although primarily for youngsters, this cannot fail to interest readers of all ages. 48 illustrations in the text. 23 photographs. 99pp. 6⅛ x 9¼.　　　　　　　　　　　　　　　　　　　　　　　　T161 Paperbound **$1.00**

BRIDGES AND THEIR BUILDERS, David Steinman and Sara Ruth Watson. Engineers, historians, everyone who has ever been fascinated by great spans will find this book an endless source of information and interest. Dr. Steinman, recipient of the Louis Levy medal, was one of the great bridge architects and engineers of all time, and his analysis of the great bridges of history is both authoritative and easily followed. Greek and Roman bridges, medieval bridges, Oriental bridges, modern works such as the Brooklyn Bridge and the Golden Gate Bridge, and many others are described in terms of history, constructional principles, artistry, and function. All in all this book is the most comprehensive and accurate semipopular history of bridges in print in English. New, greatly revised, enlarged edition. 23 photographs, 26 line drawings. Index. xvii + 401pp. 5⅜ x 8.   T431 Paperbound **$2.00**

FADS AND FALLACIES IN THE NAME OF SCIENCE, Martin Gardner. Examines various cults, quack systems, frauds, delusions which at various times have masqueraded as science. Accounts of hollow-earth fanatics like Symmes; Velikovsky and wandering planets; Hoerbiger; Bellamy and the theory of multiple moons; Charles Fort; dowsing, pseudoscientific methods for finding water, ores, oil. Sections on naturopathy, iridiagnosis, zone therapy, food fads, etc. Analytical accounts of Wilhelm Reich and orgone sex energy; L. Ron Hubbard and Dianetics; A. Korzybski and General Semantics; many others. Brought up to date to include Bridey Murphy, others. Not just a collection of anecdotes, but a fair, reasoned appraisal of eccentric theory. Formerly titled IN THE NAME OF SCIENCE. Preface. Index. x + 384pp. 5⅜ x 8.   T394 Paperbound **$1.50**

See also: A PHILOSOPHICAL ESSAY ON PROBABILITIES, P. de Laplace; ON MATHEMATICS AND MATHEMATICIANS, R. E. Moritz; AN ELEMENTARY SURVEY OF CELESTIAL MECHANICS, Y. Ryabov; THE SKY AND ITS MYSTERIES, E. A. Beet; THE REALM OF THE NEBULAE, E. Hubble; OUT OF THE SKY, H. H. Nininger; SATELLITES AND SCIENTIFIC RESEARCH, D. King-Hele; HEREDITY AND YOUR LIFE, A. M. Winchester; INSECTS AND INSECT LIFE, S. W. Frost; PRINCIPLES OF STRATIGRAPHY, A. W. Grabau; TEACH YOURSELF SERIES.

HISTORY OF SCIENCE AND MATHEMATICS

DIALOGUES CONCERNING TWO NEW SCIENCES, Galileo Galilei. This classic of experimental science, mechanics, engineering, is as enjoyable as it is important. A great historical document giving insights into one of the world's most original thinkers, it is based on 30 years' experimentation. It offers a lively exposition of dynamics, elasticity, sound, ballistics, strength of materials, the scientific method. "Superior to everything else of mine," Galileo. Trans. by H. Crew, A. Salvio. 126 diagrams. Index. xxi + 288pp. 5⅜ x 8.
                                                                              S99 Paperbound **$1.65**

A DIDEROT PICTORIAL ENCYCLOPEDIA OF TRADES AND INDUSTRY, Manufacturing and the Technical Arts in Plates Selected from "L'Encyclopédie ou Dictionnaire Raisonné des Sciences, des Arts, et des Métiers" of Denis Diderot. Edited with text by C. Gillispie. This first modern selection of plates from the high point of 18th century French engraving is a storehouse of valuable technological information to the historian of arts and science. Over 2000 illustrations on 485 full page plates, most of them original size, show the trades and industries of a fascinating era in such great detail that the processes and shops might very well be reconstructed from them. The plates teem with life, with men, women, and children performing all of the thousands of operations necessary to the trades before and during the early stages of the industrial revolution. Plates are in sequence, and show general operations, closeups of difficult operations, and details of complex machinery. Such important and interesting trades and industries are illustrated as sowing, harvesting, beekeeping, cheesemaking, operating windmills, milling flour, charcoal burning, tobacco processing, indigo, fishing, arts of war, salt extraction, mining, smelting, casting iron, steel, extracting mercury, zinc, sulphur, copper, etc., slating, tinning, silverplating, gilding, making gunpowder, cannons, bells, shoeing horses, tanning, papermaking, printing, dyeing, and more than 40 other categories. Professor Gillispie, of Princeton, supplies a full commentary on all the plates, identifying operations, tools, processes, etc. This material, presented in a lively and lucid fashion, is of great interest to the reader interested in history of science and technology. Heavy library cloth. 920pp. 9 x 12.   T421 Two volume set **$18.50**

DE MAGNETE, William Gilbert. This classic work on magnetism founded a new science. Gilbert was the first to use the word "electricity", to recognize mass as distinct from weight, to discover the effect of heat on magnetic bodies; invent an electroscope, differentiate between static electricity and magnetism, conceive of the earth as a magnet. Written by the first great experimental scientist, this lively work is valuable not only as an historical landmark, but as the delightfully easy to follow record of a perpetually searching, ingenious mind. Translated by P. F. Mottelay. 25 page biographical memoir. 90 figures. lix + 368pp. 5⅜ x 8.   S470 Paperbound **$2.00**

CHARLES BABBAGE AND HIS CALCULATING ENGINES, edited by P. Morrison and E. Morrison. Babbage, leading 19th century pioneer in mathematical machines and herald of modern operational research, was the true father of Harvard's relay computer Mark I. His Difference Engine and Analytical Engine were the first machines in the field. This volume contains a valuable introduction on his life and work; major excerpts from his autobiography, revealing his eccentric and unusual personality; and extensive selections from "Babbage's Calculating Engines," a compilation of hard-to-find journal articles by Babbage, the Countess of Lovelace, L. F. Menabrea, and Dionysius Lardner. 8 illustrations, Appendix of miscellaneous papers. Index. Bibliography. xxxviii + 400pp. 5⅜ x 8.   T12 Paperbound **$2.00**

A HISTORY OF ASTRONOMY FROM THALES TO KEPLER, J. L. E. Dreyer. (Formerly A HISTORY OF PLANETARY SYSTEMS FROM THALES TO KEPLER.) This is the only work in English to give the complete history of man's cosmological views from prehistoric times to Kepler and Newton. Partial contents: Near Eastern astronomical systems, Early Greeks, Homocentric Spheres of Eudoxus, Epicycles, Ptolemaic system, medieval cosmology, Copernicus, Kepler, etc. Revised, foreword by W. H. Stahl. New bibliography. xvii + 430pp. 5⅜ x 8.
S79 Paperbound **$1.98**

A SHORT HISTORY OF ANATOMY AND PHYSIOLOGY FROM THE GREEKS TO HARVEY, Charles Singer. Corrected edition of THE EVOLUTION OF ANATOMY, classic work tracing evolution of anatomy and physiology from prescientific times through Greek & Roman periods, Dark Ages, Renaissance, to age of Harvey and beginning of modern concepts. Centered on individuals, movements, periods that definitely advanced anatomical knowledge: Plato, Diocles, Aristotle, Theophrastus, Herophilus, Erasistratus, the Alexandrians, Galen, Mondino, da Vinci, Linacre, Sylvius, others. Special section on Vesalius; Vesalian atlas of nudes, skeletons, muscle tabulae. Index of names, 20 plates. 270 extremely interesting illustrations of ancient, medieval, Renaissance, Oriental origin. xii + 209pp. 5⅜ x 8.   T389 Paperbound **$1.75**

FROM MAGIC TO SCIENCE, Charles Singer. A great historian examines aspects of medical science from the Roman Empire through the Renaissance. Includes perhaps the best discussion of early herbals, and a penetrating physiological interpretation of "The Visions of Hildegarde of Bingen." Also examined are Arabian and Galenic influences; the Sphere of Pythagoras; Paracelsus; the reawakening of science under Leonardo da Vinci, Vesalius; the Lorica of Gildas the Briton; etc. Frequent quotations with translations. New Introduction by the author. New unabridged, corrected edition. 158 unusual illustrations from classical and medieval sources. Index. xxvii + 365pp. 5⅜ x 8.   T390 Paperbound **$2.00**

HISTORY OF MATHEMATICS, D. E. Smith. Most comprehensive non-technical history of math in English. Discusses lives and works of over a thousand major and minor figures, with footnotes supplying technical information outside the book's scheme, and indicating disputed matters. Vol I: A chronological examination, from primitive concepts through Egypt, Babylonia, Greece, the Orient, Rome, the Middle Ages, the Renaissance, and up to 1900. Vol 2: The development of ideas in specific fields and problems, up through elementary calculus. Two volumes, total of 510 illustrations, 1355pp. 5⅜ x 8. Set boxed in attractive container.   T429, 430 Paperbound, the set **$5.00**

A SHORT ACCOUNT OF THE HISTORY OF MATHEMATICS, W. W. R. Ball. Most readable non-technical history of mathematics treats lives, discoveries of every important figure from Egyptian, Phoenician mathematicians to late 19th century. Discusses schools of Ionia, Pythagoras, Athens, Cyzicus, Alexandria, Byzantium, systems of numeration; primitive arithmetic; Middle Ages, Renaissance, including Arabs, Bacon, Regiomontanus, Tartaglia, Cardan, Stevinus, Galileo, Kepler; modern mathematics of Descartes, Pascal, Wallis, Huygens, Newton, Leibnitz, d'Alembert, Euler, Lambert, Laplace, Legendre, Gauss, Hermite, Weierstrass, scores more. Index. 25 figures. 546pp. 5⅜ x 8.   S630 Paperbound **$2.00**

A SOURCE BOOK IN MATHEMATICS, D. E. Smith. Great discoveries in math, from Renaissance to end of 19th century, in English translation. Read announcements by Dedekind, Gauss, Delamain, Pascal, Fermat, Newton, Abel, Lobachevsky, Bolyai, Riemann, De Moivre, Legendre, Laplace, others of discoveries about imaginary numbers, number congruence, slide rule, equations, symbolism, cubic algebraic equations, non-Euclidean forms of geometry, calculus, function theory, quaternions, etc. Succinct selections from 125 different treatises, articles, most unavailable elsewhere in English. Each article preceded by biographical, historical introduction. Vol. I: Fields of Number, Algebra. Index. 32 illus. 338pp. 5⅜ x 8. Vol. II: Fields of Geometry, Probability, Calculus, Functions, Quaternions. 83 illus. 432pp. 5⅜ x 8.
Vol. 1: S552 Paperbound **$1.85**
Vol. 2: S553 Paperbound **$1.85**
2 vol. set, boxed **$3.50**

A HISTORY OF THE CALCULUS, AND ITS CONCEPTUAL DEVELOPMENT, Carl B. Boyer. Provides laymen and mathematicians a detailed history of the development of the calculus, from early beginning in antiquity to final elaboration as mathematical abstractions. Gives a sense of mathematics not as a technique, but as a habit of mind, in the progression of ideas of Zeno, Plato, Pythagoras, Eudoxus, Arabic and Scholastic mathematicians, Newton, Leibnitz, Taylor, Descartes, Euler, Lagrange, Cantor, Weierstrass, and others. This first comprehensive critical history of the calculus was originally titled "The Concepts of the Calculus." Foreword by R. Courant. Preface. 22 figures. 25-page bibliography. Index. v + 364pp. 5⅜ x 8.   S509 Paperbound **$2.00**

A CONCISE HISTORY OF MATHEMATICS, D. Struik. Lucid study of development of mathematical ideas, techniques from Ancient Near East, Greece, Islamic science, Middle Ages, Renaissance, modern times. Important mathematicians are described in detail. Treatment is not anecdotal, but analytical development of ideas. "Rich in content, thoughtful in interpretation," U.S. QUARTERLY BOOKLIST. Non-technical; no mathematical training needed. Index. 60 illustrations, including Egyptian papyri, Greek mss., portraits of 31 eminent mathematicians. Bibliography. 2nd edition. xix + 299pp. 5⅜ x 8.   T255 Paperbound **$1.75**

See also: **NON-EUCLIDEAN GEOMETRY, R. Bonola; THEORY OF DETERMINANTS IN HISTORICAL ORDER OF DEVELOPMENT, T. Muir; HISTORY OF THE THEORY OF ELASTICITY AND STRENGTH OF MATERIALS, I. Todhunter and K. Pearson; A SHORT HISTORY OF ASTRONOMY, A. Berry; CLASSICS OF SCIENCE.**

PHILOSOPHY OF SCIENCE AND MATHEMATICS

FOUNDATIONS OF SCIENCE: THE PHILOSOPHY OF THEORY AND EXPERIMENT, N. R. Campbell. A critique of the most fundamental concepts of science in general and physics in particular. Examines why certain propositions are accepted without question, demarcates science from philosophy, clarifies the understanding of the tools of science. Part One analyzes the presuppositions of scientific thought: existence of the material world, nature of scientific laws, multiplication of probabilities, etc.: Part Two covers the nature of experiment and the application of mathematics: conditions for measurement, relations between numerical laws and theories, laws of error, etc. An appendix covers problems arising from relativity, force, motion, space, and time. A classic in its field. Index. xiii + 565pp. 5⅝ x 8⅜.
S372 Paperbound **$2.95**

WHAT IS SCIENCE?, Norman Campbell. This excellent introduction explains scientific method, role of mathematics, types of scientific laws. Contents: 2 aspects of science, science & nature, laws of science, discovery of laws, explanation of laws, measurement & numerical laws, applications of science. 192pp. 5⅜ x 8.   S43 Paperbound **$1.25**

THE VALUE OF SCIENCE, Henri Poincaré. Many of the most mature ideas of the "last scientific universalist" covered with charm and vigor for both the beginning student and the advanced worker. Discusses the nature of scientific truth, whether order is innate in the universe or imposed upon it by man, logical thought versus intuition (relating to math, through the works of Weierstrass, Lie, Klein, Riemann), time and space (relativity, psychological time, simultaneity), Hertz's concept of force, interrelationship of mathematical physics to pure math, values within disciplines of Maxwell, Carnot, Mayer, Newton, Lorentz, etc. Index. iii + 147pp. 5⅜ x 8.   S469 Paperbound **$1.35**

SCIENCE AND METHOD, Henri Poincaré. Procedure of scientific discovery, methodology, experiment, idea-germination—the intellectual processes by which discoveries come into being. Most significant and most interesting aspects of development, application of ideas. Chapters cover selection of facts, chance, mathematical reasoning, mathematics, and logic; Whitehead, Russell, Cantor; the new mechanics, etc. 288pp. 5⅜ x 8.   S222 Paperbound **$1.35**

SCIENCE AND HYPOTHESIS, Henri Poincaré. Creative psychology in science. How such concepts as number, magnitude, space, force, classical mechanics were developed, and how the modern scientist uses them in his thought. Hypothesis in physics, theories of modern physics. Introduction by Sir James Larmor. "Few mathematicians have had the breadth of vision of Poincaré, and none is his superior in the gift of clear exposition," E. T. Bell. Index. 272pp. 5⅜ x 8.   S221 Paperbound **$1.35**

PHILOSOPHY AND THE PHYSICISTS, L. S. Stebbing. The philosophical aspects of modern science examined in terms of a lively critical attack on the ideas of Jeans and Eddington. Discusses the task of science, causality, determinism, probability, consciousness, the relation of the world of physics to that of everyday experience. Probes the philosophical significance of the Planck-Bohr concept of discontinuous energy levels, the inferences to be drawn from Heisenberg's Uncertainty Principle, the implications of "becoming" involved in the 2nd law of thermodynamics, and other problems posed by the discarding of Laplacean determinism. 285pp. 5⅜ x 8.   T480 Paperbound **$1.65**

EXPERIMENT AND THEORY IN PHYSICS, Max Born. A Nobel laureate examines the nature and value of the counterclaims of experiment and theory in physics. Synthetic versus analytical scientific advances are analyzed in the work of Einstein, Bohr, Heisenberg, Planck, Eddington, Milne, and others by a fellow participant. 44pp. 5⅜ x 8.   S308 Paperbound 60¢

THE NATURE OF PHYSICAL THEORY, P. W. Bridgman. Here is how modern physics looks to a highly unorthodox physicist—a Nobel laureate. Pointing out many absurdities of science, and demonstrating the inadequacies of various physical theories, Dr. Bridgman weighs and analyzes the contributions of Einstein, Bohr, Newton, Heisenberg, and many others. This is a non-technical consideration of the correlation of science and reality. Index. xi + 138pp. 5⅜ x 8.
S33 Paperbound $1.25

THE PHILOSOPHY OF SPACE AND TIME, H. Reichenbach. An important landmark in the development of the empiricist conception of geometry, covering the problem of the foundations of geometry, the theory of time, the consequences of Einstein's relativity, including: relations between theory and observations; coordinate and metrical properties of space; the psychological problem of visual intuition of non-Euclidean structures; and many other important topics in modern science and philosophy. The majority of ideas require only a knowledge of intermediate math. Introduction by R. Carnap. 49 figures. Index. xviii + 296pp. 5⅜ x 8.
S443 Paperbound $2.00

MATTER & MOTION, James Clerk Maxwell, This excellent exposition begins with simple particles and proceeds gradually to physical systems beyond complete analysis: motion, force, properties of centre of mass of material system, work, energy, gravitation, etc. Written with all Maxwell's original insights and clarity. Notes by E. Larmor. 17 diagrams. 178pp. 5⅜ x 8.
S188 Paperbound $1.35

THE ANALYSIS OF MATTER, Bertrand Russell. How do our senses concord with the new physics? This volume covers such topics as logical analysis of physics, prerelativity physics, causality, scientific inference, physics and perception, special and general relativity, Weyl's theory, tensors, invariants and their physical interpretation, periodicity and qualitative series. "The most thorough treatment of the subject that has yet been published," THE NATION. Introduction by L. E. Denonn. 422pp. 5⅜ x 8.
T231 Paperbound $1.95

SUBSTANCE AND FUNCTION, & EINSTEIN'S THEORY OF RELATIVITY, Ernst Cassirer. Two books bound as one. Cassirer establishes a philosophy of the exact sciences that takes into consideration newer developments in mathematics, and also shows historical connections. Partial contents: Aristotelian logic, Mill's analysis, Helmholtz & Kronecker, Russell & cardinal numbers, Euclidean vs. non-Euclidean geometry, Einstein's relativity. Bibliography. Index. xxi + 465pp. 5⅜ x 8.
T50 Paperbound $2.00

PRINCIPLES OF MECHANICS, Heinrich Hertz. This last work by the great 19th century physicist is not only a classic, but of great interest in the logic of science. Creating a new system of mechanics based upon space, time, and mass, it returns to axiomatic analysis, to understanding of the formal or structural aspects of science, taking into account logic, observation, and a priori elements. Of great historical importance to Poincaré, Carnap, Einstein, Milne. A 20-page introduction by R. S. Cohen, Wesleyan University, analyzes the implications of Hertz's thought and the logic of science. Bibliography. 13-page introduction by Helmholtz. xlii + 274pp. 5⅜ x 8.
S316 Clothbound $3.50
S317 Paperbound $1.85

THE PHILOSOPHICAL WRITINGS OF PEIRCE, edited by Justus Buchler. (Formerly published as THE PHILOSOPHY OF PEIRCE.) This is a carefully balanced exposition of Peirce's complete system, written by Peirce himself. It covers such matters as scientific method, pure chance vs. law, symbolic logic, theory of signs, pragmatism, experiment, and other topics. Introduction by Justus Buchler, Columbia University. xvi + 368pp. 5⅜ x 8.
T217 Paperbound $1.95

ESSAYS IN EXPERIMENTAL LOGIC, John Dewey. This stimulating series of essays touches upon the relationship between inquiry and experience, dependence of knowledge upon thought, character of logic; judgments of practice, data and meanings, stimuli of thought, etc. Index. viii + 444pp. 5⅜ x 8.
T73 Paperbound $1.95

LANGUAGE, TRUTH AND LOGIC, A. Ayer. A clear introduction to the Vienna and Cambridge schools of Logical Positivism. It sets up specific tests by which you can evaluate validity of ideas, etc. Contents: Function of philosophy, elimination of metaphysics, nature of analysis, a priori, truth and probability, etc. 10th printing. "I should like to have written it myself," Bertrand Russell. Index. 160pp. 5⅜ x 8.
T10 Paperbound $1.25

THE PSYCHOLOGY OF INVENTION IN THE MATHEMATICAL FIELD, J. Hadamard. Where do ideas come from? What role does the unconscious play? Are ideas best developed by mathematical reasoning, word reasoning, visualization? What are the methods used by Einstein, Poincaré, Galton, Riemann? How can these techniques be applied by others? Hadamard, one of the world's leading mathematicians, discusses these and other questions. xiii + 145pp. 5⅜ x 8.
T107 Paperbound $1.25

FOUNDATIONS OF GEOMETRY, Bertrand Russell. Analyzing basic problems in the overlap area between mathematics and philosophy, Nobel laureate Russell examines the nature of geometrical knowledge, the nature of geometry, and the application of geometry to space. It covers the history of non-Euclidean geometry, philosophic interpretations of geometry—especially Kant—projective and metrical geometry. This is most interesting as the solution offered in 1897 by a great mind to a problem still current. New introduction by Prof. Morris Kline of N. Y. University. xii + 201pp. 5⅜ x 8.
S232 Clothbound $3.25
S233 Paperbound $1.60

BIBLIOGRAPHIES

GUIDE TO THE LITERATURE OF MATHEMATICS AND PHYSICS, N. G. Parke III. Over 5000 entries included under approximately 120 major subject headings, of selected most important books, monographs, periodicals, articles in English, plus important works in German, French, Italian, Spanish, Russian (many recently available works). Covers every branch of physics, math, related engineering. Includes author, title, edition, publisher, place, date, number of volumes, number of pages. A 40-page introduction on the basic problems of research and study provides useful information on the organization and use of libraries, the psychology of learning, etc. This reference work will save you hours of time. 2nd revised edition. Indices of authors, subjects. 464pp. 5⅜ x 8. **S447 Paperbound $2.49**

THE STUDY OF THE HISTORY OF MATHEMATICS & THE STUDY OF THE HISTORY OF SCIENCE, George Sarton. Scientific method & philosophy in 2 scholarly fields. Defines duty of historian of math., provides especially useful bibliography with best available biographies of modern mathematicians, editions of their collected works, correspondence. Observes combination of history & science, will aid scholar in understanding science today. Bibliography includes best known treatises on historical methods. 200-item critically evaluated bibliography. Index. 10 illustrations. 2 volumes bound as one. 113pp. + 75pp. 5⅜ x 8. **T240 Paperbound $1.25**

MATHEMATICAL PUZZLES

AMUSEMENTS IN MATHEMATICS, Henry Ernest Dudeney. The foremost British originator of mathematical puzzles is always intriguing, witty, and paradoxical in this classic, one of the largest collections of mathematical amusements. More than 430 puzzles, problems, and paradoxes. Mazes and games, problems on number manipulation, unicursal and other route problems, puzzles on measuring, weighing, packing, age, kinship, chessboards, joiners', crossing river, plane figure dissection, and many others. Solutions. More than 450 illustrations. vii + 258pp. 5⅜ x 8. **T473 Paperbound $1.25**

THE CANTERBURY PUZZLES, Henry Ernest Dudeney. Chaucer's pilgrims set one another problems in story form. Also Adventures of the Puzzle Club, the Strange Escape of the King's Jester, the Monks of Riddlewell, the Squire's Christmas Puzzle Party, and others. All puzzles are original, based on dissecting plane figures, arithmetic, algebra, elementary calculus, and other branches of mathematics, and purely logical ingenuity. "The limit of ingenuity and intricacy . . ." The Observer. Over 110 puzzles. Full solutions. 150 illustrations. viii + 225pp. 5⅜ x 8. **T474 Paperbound $1.25**

SYMBOLIC LOGIC and THE GAME OF LOGIC, Lewis Carroll. "Symbolic Logic" is not concerned with modern symbolic logic, but is instead a collection of over 380 problems posed with charm and imagination, using the syllogism, and a fascinating diagrammatic method of drawing conclusions. In "The Game of Logic," Carroll's whimsical imagination devises a logical game played with 2 diagrams and counters (included) to manipulate hundreds of tricky syllogisms. The final section, "Hit or Miss" is a lagniappe of 101 additional puzzles in the delightful Carroll manner. Until this reprint edition, both of these books were rarities costing up to $15 each. Symbolic Logic: Index, xxxi + 199pp. The Game of Logic: 96pp. Two vols. bound as one. 5⅜ x 8. **T492 Paperbound $1.50**

PILLOW PROBLEMS and A TANGLED TALE, Lewis Carroll. One of the rarest of all Carroll's works, "Pillow Problems" contains 72 original math puzzles, all typically ingenious. Particularly fascinating are Carroll's answers which remain exactly as he thought them out, reflecting his actual mental processes. The problems in "A Tangled Tale" are in story form, originally appearing as a monthly magazine serial. Carroll not only gives the solutions, but uses answers sent in by readers to discuss wrong approaches and misleading paths, and grades them for insight. Both of these books were rarities until this edition, "Pillow Problems" costing up to $25, and "A Tangled Tale" $15. Pillow Problems: Preface and introduction by Lewis Carroll. xx + 109pp. A Tangled Tale: 6 illustrations. 152pp. Two vols. bound as one. 5⅜ x 8. **T493 Paperbound $1.50**

DIVERSIONS AND DIGRESSIONS OF LEWIS CARROLL. A major new treasure for Carroll fans! Rare privately published puzzles, mathematical amusements and recreations, games. Includes the fragmentary Part III of "Curiosa Mathematica." Also contains humorous and satirical pieces: "The New Belfry," "The Vision of the Three T's," and much more. New 32-page supplement of rare photographs taken by Carroll. Formerly titled "The Lewis Carroll Picture Book." Edited by S. Collingwood. x + 375pp. 5⅜ x 8. **T732 Paperbound $1.50**

CHEMISTRY AND PHYSICAL CHEMISTRY

ORGANIC CHEMISTRY, F. C. Whitmore. The entire subject of organic chemistry for the practic-ing chemist and the advanced student. Storehouse of facts, theories, processes found else-where only in specialized journals. Covers aliphatic compounds (500 pages on the properties and synthetic preparation of hydrocarbons, halides, proteins, ketones, etc.), alicyclic com-pounds, aromatic compounds, heterocyclic compounds, organophosphorus and organometallic compounds. Methods of synthetic preparation analyzed critically throughout. Includes much of biochemical interest. "The scope of this volume is astonishing," INDUSTRIAL AND ENGINEER-ING CHEMISTRY. 12,000-reference index. 2387-item bibliography. Total of x + 1005pp. 5⅜ x 8. Two volume set.
S700 Vol I Paperbound **$2.00**
S701 Vol II Paperbound **$2.00**
The set **$4.00**

THE PRINCIPLES OF ELECTROCHEMISTRY, D. A. MacInnes. Basic equations for almost every subfield of electrochemistry from first principles, referring at all times to the soundest and most recent theories and results; unusually useful as text or as reference. Covers coulometers and Faraday's Law, electrolytic conductance, the Debye-Hueckel method for the theoretical calculation of activity coefficients, concentration cells, standard electrode potentials, thermo-dynamic ionization constants, pH, potentiometric titrations, irreversible phenomena, Planck's equation, and much more. "Excellent treatise," AMERICAN CHEMICAL SOCIETY JOURNAL. "Highly recommended," CHEMICAL AND METALLURGICAL ENGINEERING. 2 Indices. Appendix. 585-item bibliography. 137 figures. 94 tables. ii + 478pp. 5⅝ x 8⅜.
S52 Paperbound **$2.35**

THE CHEMISTRY OF URANIUM: THE ELEMENT, ITS BINARY AND RELATED COMPOUNDS, J. J. Katz and E. Rabinowitch. Vast post-World War II collection and correlation of thousands of AEC reports and published papers in a useful and easily accessible form, still the most complete and up-to-date compilation. Treats "dry uranium chemistry," occurrences, preparation, prop-erties, simple compounds, isotopic composition, extraction from ores, spectra, alloys, etc. Much material available only here. Index. Thousands of evaluated bibliographical references. 324 tables, charts, figures. xxi + 609pp. 5⅜ x 8.
S757 Paperbound **$2.95**

KINETIC THEORY OF LIQUIDS, J. Frenkel. Regarding the kinetic theory of liquids as a gen-eralization and extension of the theory of solid bodies, this volume covers all types of arrangements of solids, thermal displacements of atoms, interstitial atoms and ions, orientational and rotational motion of molecules, and transition between states of matter. Mathematical theory is developed close to the physical subject matter. 216 bibliographical footnotes. 55 figures. xi + 485pp. 5⅜ x 8.
S94 Clothbound **$3.95**
S95 Paperbound **$2.45**

POLAR MOLECULES, Pieter Debye. This work by Nobel laureate Debye offers a complete guide to fundamental electrostatic field relations, polarizability, molecular structure. Partial con-tents: electric intensity, displacement and force, polarization by orientation, molar polariza-tion and molar refraction, halogen-hydrides, polar liquids, ionic saturation, dielectric con-stant, etc. Special chapter considers quantum theory. Indexed. 172pp. 5⅜ x 8.
S64 Paperbound **$1.50**

ELASTICITY, PLASTICITY AND STRUCTURE OF MATTER, R. Houwink. Standard treatise on rheological aspects of different technically important solids such as crystals, resins, textiles, rubber, clay, many others. Investigates general laws for deformations; determines divergences from these laws for certain substances. Covers general physical and mathematical aspects of plasticity, elasticity, viscosity. Detailed examination of deformations, internal structure of matter in relation to elastic and plastic behavior, formation of solid matter from a fluid, conditions for elastic and plastic behavior of matter. Treats glass, asphalt, gutta percha, balata, proteins, baker's dough, lacquers, sulphur, others. 2nd revised, enlarged edition. Extensive revised bibliography in over 500 footnotes. Index. Table of symbols. 214 figures. xviii + 368pp. 6 x 9¼.
S385 Paperbound **$2.45**

THE PHASE RULE AND ITS APPLICATION, Alexander Findlay. Covering chemical phenomena of 1, 2, 3, 4, and multiple component systems, this "standard work on the subject" (NATURE, London), has been completely revised and brought up to date by A. N. Campbell and N. O. Smith. Brand new material has been added on such matters as binary, tertiary liquid equilibria, solid solutions in ternary systems, quinary systems of salts and water. Completely revised to triangular coordinates in ternary systems, clarified graphic repre-sentation, solid models, etc. 9th revised edition. Author, subject indexes. 236 figures. 505 footnotes, mostly bibliographic. xii + 494pp. 5⅜ x 8.
S91 Paperbound **$2.45**

TERNARY SYSTEMS: INTRODUCTION TO THE THEORY OF THREE COMPONENT SYSTEMS, G. Masing. Furnishes detailed discussion of representative types of 3-components systems, both in solid models (particularly metallic alloys) and isothermal models. Discusses mechanical mixture without compounds and without solid solutions; unbroken solid solution series; solid solutions with solubility breaks in two binary systems; iron-silicon-aluminum alloys; allotropic forms of iron in ternary system; other topics. Bibliography. Index. 166 illustrations. 178pp. 5⅝ x 8⅜. S631 Paperbound **$1.45**

THE STORY OF ALCHEMY AND EARLY CHEMISTRY, J. M. Stillman. An authoritative, scholarly work, highly readable, of development of chemical knowledge from 4000 B.C. to downfall of phlogiston theory in late 18th century. Every important figure, many quotations. Brings alive curious, almost incredible history of alchemical beliefs, practices, writings of Arabian Prince Oneeyade, Vincent of Beauvais, Geber, Zosimos, Paracelsus, Vitruvius, scores more. Studies work, thought of Black, Cavendish, Priestley, Van Helmont, Bergman, Lavoisier, Newton, etc. Index. Bibliography. 579pp. 5⅜ x 8. S628 Paperbound **$2.45**

See also: **ATOMIC SPECTRA AND ATOMIC STRUCTURE, G. Herzberg; INVESTIGATIONS ON THE THEORY OF THE BROWNIAN MOVEMENT, A. Einstein; TREATISE ON THERMODYNAMICS, M. Planck.**

ASTRONOMY AND ASTROPHYSICS

AN ELEMENTARY SURVEY OF CELESTIAL MECHANICS, Y. Ryabov. Elementary exposition of gravitational theory and celestial mechanics. Historical introduction and coverage of basic principles, including: the elliptic, the orbital plane, the 2- and 3-body problems, the discovery of Neptune, planetary rotation, the length of the day, the shapes of galaxies, satellites (detailed treatment of Sputnik I), etc. First American reprinting of successful Russian popular exposition. Elementary algebra and trigonometry helpful, but not necessary; presentation chiefly verbal. Appendix of theorem proofs. 58 figures. 165pp. 5⅜ x 8. T756 Paperbound **$1.25**

THE SKY AND ITS MYSTERIES, E. A. Beet. One of most lucid books on mysteries of universe; deals with astronomy from earliest observations to latest theories of expansion of universe, source of stellar energy, birth of planets, origin of moon craters, possibility of life on other planets. Discusses effects of sunspots on weather; distances, ages of several stars; master plan of universe; methods and tools of astronomers; much more. "Eminently readable book," London Times. Extensive bibliography. Over 50 diagrams. 12 full-page plates, fold-out star map. Introduction. Index, 238pp. 5¼ x 7½. T627 Clothbound **$3.00**

THE REALM OF THE NEBULAE, E. Hubble. One of the great astronomers of our time records his formulation of the concept of "island universes," and its impact on astronomy. Such topics are covered as the velocity-distance relation; classification, nature, distances, general field of nebulae; cosmological theories; nebulae in the neighborhood of the Milky Way. 39 photos of nebulae, nebulae clusters, spectra of nebulae, and velocity distance relations shown by spectrum comparison. "One of the most progressive lines of astronomical research," The Times (London). New introduction by A. Sandage. 55 illustrations. Index. iv + 201pp. 5⅜ x 8. S455 Paperbound **$1.50**

OUT OF THE SKY, H. H. Nininger. A non-technical but comprehensive introduction to "meteoritics", the young science concerned with all aspects of the arrival of matter from outer space. Written by one of the world's experts on meteorites, this work shows how, despite difficulties of observation and sparseness of data, a considerable body of knowledge has arisen. It defines meteors and meteorites; studies fireball clusters and processions, meteorite composition, size, distribution, showers, explosions, origins, craters, and much more. A true connecting link between astronomy and geology. More than 175 photos, 22 other illustrations. References. Bibliography of author's publications on meteorites. Index. viii + 336pp. 5⅜ x 8. T519 Paperbound **$1.85**

SATELLITES AND SCIENTIFIC RESEARCH, D. King-Hele. Non-technical account of the manmade satellites and the discoveries they have yielded up to the spring of 1959. Brings together information hitherto published only in hard-to-get scientific journals. Includes the life history of a typical satellite, methods of tracking, new information on the shape of the earth, zones of radiation, etc. Over 60 diagrams and 6 photographs. Mathematical appendix. Bibliography of over 100 items. Index. xii + 180pp. 5⅜ x 8½. T703 Clothbound **$4.00**

HOW TO MAKE A TELESCOPE, Jean Texereau. Enables the most inexperienced to choose, design, and build an f/6 or f/8 Newtonian type reflecting telescope, with an altazimuth Couder mounting, suitable for lunar, planetary, and stellar observation. A practical step-by-step course covering every operation and every piece of equipment. Basic principles of geometric and physical optics are discussed (though unnecessary to construction), and the merits of reflectors and refractors compared. A thorough discussion of eyepieces, finders, grinding, installation, testing, using the instrument, etc. 241 figures and 38 photos show almost every operation and tool. Potential errors are anticipated as much as possible. Foreword by A. Couder. Bibliography and sources of supply listing. Index. xiii + 191pp. 6¼ x 10. T464 Clothbound **$3.50**

AN INTRODUCTORY TREATISE ON DYNAMICAL ASTRONOMY, H. C. Plummer. Unusually wide connected and concise coverage of nearly every significant branch of dynamical astronomy, stressing basic principles throughout: determination of orbits, planetary theory, lunar theory, precession and nutation, and many of their applications. Hundreds of formulas and theorems worked out completely, important methods thoroughly explained. Covers motion under a central attraction, orbits of double stars and spectroscopic binaries, the libration of the moon, and much more. Index. 8 diagrams. xxi + 343pp. 5⅝ x 8⅜. S689 Paperbound **$2.35**

A COMPENDIUM OF SPHERICAL ASTRONOMY, S. Newcomb. Long a standard collection of basic methods and formulas most useful to the working astronomer, and clear full text for students. Includes the most important common approximations; 40 pages on the method of least squares; general theory of spherical coordinates; parallax; aberration; astronomical refraction; theory of precession; proper motion of the stars; methods of deriving positions of stars; and much more. Index. 9 Appendices of tables, formulas, etc. 36 figures. xviii + 444pp. 5⅜ x 8.
S690 Paperbound **$2.25**

AN INTRODUCTORY TREATISE ON THE LUNAR THEORY, E. W. Brown. Indispensable for all scientists and engineers interested in orbital calculation, satellites, or navigation of space. Only work in English to explain in detail 5 major mathematical approaches to the problem of 3 bodies, those of Laplace, de Pontécoulant, Hansen, Delaunay, and Hill. Covers expressions for mutual attraction, equations of motion, forms of solution, variations of the elements in disturbed motion, the constants and their interpretations, planetary and other disturbing influences, etc. Index. Bibliography. Tables. xvi + 292pp. 5⅝ x 8⅜.
S666 Paperbound **$2.00**

LES METHODES NOUVELLES DE LA MECANIQUE CELESTE, H. Poincaré. Complete text (in French) of one of Poincaré's most important works. This set revolutionized celestial mechanics: first use of integral invariants, first major application of linear differential equations, study of periodic orbits, lunar motion and Jupiter's satellites, three body problem, and many other important topics. "Started a new era . . . so extremely modern that even today few have mastered his weapons," E. T. Bell. Three volumes. Total 1282pp. 6⅛ x 9¼.
Vol. 1. S401 Paperbound **$2.75**
Vol. 2. S402 Paperbound **$2.75**
Vol. 3. S403 Paperbound **$2.75**
The set **$7.50**

SPHERICAL AND PRACTICAL ASTRONOMY, W. Chauvenet. First book in English to apply mathematical techniques to astronomical problems is still standard work. Covers almost entire field, rigorously, with over 300 examples worked out, Vol. 1, spherical astronomy, applications to nautical astronomy; determination of hour angles, parallactic angle for known stars; interpolation; parallax; laws of refraction; predicting eclipses; precession, nutation of fixed stars; etc. Vol. 2, theory, use, of instruments; telescope; measurement of arcs, angles in general; electro-chronograph; sextant, reflecting circles; zenith telescope; etc. 100-page appendix of detailed proof of Gauss' method of least squares. 5th revised edition. Index. 15 plates, 20 tables. 1340pp. 5⅜ x 8. Vol. 1 S618 Paperbound **$2.75**
Vol. 2 S619 Paperbound **$2.75**
The set **$5.50**

THE INTERNAL CONSTITUTION OF THE STARS, Sir A. S. Eddington. Influence of this has been enormous; first detailed exposition of theory of radiative equilibrium for stellar interiors, of all available evidence for existence of diffuse matter in interstellar space. Studies quantum theory, polytropic gas spheres, mass-luminosity relations, variable stars, etc. Discussions of equations paralleled with informal exposition of intimate relationship of astrophysics with great discoveries in atomic physics, radiation. Introduction. Appendix. Index. 421pp. 5⅜ x 8.
S563 Paperbound **$2.25**

ASTRONOMY OF STELLAR ENERGY AND DECAY, Martin Johnson. Middle level treatment of astronomy as interpreted by modern atomic physics. Part One is non-technical, examines physical properties, source of energy, spectroscopy, fluctuating stars, various models and theories, etc. Part Two parallels these topics, providing their mathematical foundation. "Clear, concise, and readily understandable," American Library Assoc. Bibliography. 3 indexes. 29 illustrations. 216pp. 5⅜ x 8. S537 Paperbound **$1.50**

RADIATIVE TRANSFER, S. Chandrasekhar. Definitive work in field provides foundation for analysis of stellar atmospheres, planetary illumination, sky radiation; to physicists, a study of problems analogous to those in theory of diffusion of neutrons. Partial contents: equation of transfer, isotropic scattering, H-functions, diffuse reflection and transmission, Rayleigh scattering, X, Y functions, radiative equilibrium of stellar atmospheres. Extensive bibliography. 3 appendices. 35 tables. 35 figures. 407pp. 5⅝ x 8⅜. S599 Paperbound **$2.25**

AN INTRODUCTION TO THE STUDY OF STELLAR STRUCTURE, Subrahmanyan Chandrasekhar. Outstanding treatise on stellar dynamics by one of world's greatest astrophysicists. Uses classical & modern math methods to examine relationship between loss of energy, the mass, and radius of stars in a steady state. Discusses thermodynamic laws from Caratheodory's axiomatic standpoint; adiabatic, polytropic laws; work of Ritter, Emden, Kelvin, others; Stroemgren envelopes as starter for theory of gaseous stars; Gibbs statistical mechanics (quantum); degenerate stellar configuration & theory of white dwarfs, etc. "Highest level of scientific merit," BULLETIN, AMER. MATH. SOC. Bibliography. Appendixes. Index. 33 figures. 509pp. 5⅜ x 8. S413 Paperbound **$2.75**

THREE COPERNICAN TREATISES, translated with notes by Edward Rosen. 3 papers available nowhere else in English: "The Commentariolus" and "Letter against Werner" of Copernicus; the "Narratio prima" of Rheticus. The "Commentariolus" is Copernicus's most lucid exposition of his system. The "Letter against Werner" throws light on development of Copernicus's thought. The "Narratio prima" is earliest printed presentation of the new astronomy. "Educational and enjoyable," Astrophysical Journal. Corrected edition. Biographical introduction. 877-item bibliography of virtually every book, article, on Copernicus published 1939-1958. Index. 19 illustrations. 218pp. 5⅜ x 8.   S585 Paperbound **$1.75**

EARTH SCIENCES

PRINCIPLES OF STRATIGRAPHY, A. W. Grabau. Classic of 20th century geology, unmatched in scope and comprehensiveness. Nearly 600 pages cover the structure and origins of every kind of sedimentary, hydrogenic, oceanic, pyroclastic, atmoclastic, hydroclastic, marine hydroclastic, and bioclastic rock; metamorphism; erosion; etc. Includes also the constitution of the atmosphere; morphology of oceans, rivers, glaciers; volcanic activities; faults and earthquakes; and fundamental principles of paleontology (nearly 200 pages). New introduction by Prof. M. Kay, Columbia U. 1277 bibliographical entries. 264 diagrams. Tables, maps, etc. Two volume set. Total of xxxii + 1185pp. 5⅜ x 8.   S686 Vol I Paperbound **$2.50**
S687 Vol II Paperbound **$2.50**
The set **$5.00**

THE GEOLOGICAL DRAMA, H. and G. Termier. Unusual work by 2 noted French geologists: not the usual survey of geological periods, but general principles; continent formation, the influence of ice-ages and earth movements in shaping the present-day land masses, the creation and advance of life, the position of man. Readable and authoritative survey for the layman; excellent supplement for the student of geology; important collection of recent European theories for the American geologist. Much material appears here for the first time in a non-technical work. Index. 30 photographs, 5 diagrams. 5 maps. 144pp. 6 x 9.   T702 Clothbound **$3.95**

THE EVOLUTION OF THE IGNEOUS ROCKS, N. L. Bowen. Invaluable serious introduction applies techniques of physics and chemistry to explain igneous rock diversity in terms of chemical composition and fractional crystallization. Discusses liquid immiscibility in silicate magmas, crystal sorting, liquid lines of descent, fractional resorption of complex minerals, petrogenesis, etc. Of prime importance to geologists & mining engineers, also to physicists, chemists working with high temperatures and pressures. "Most important," TIMES, London. 3 indexes. 263 bibliographic notes. 82 figures. xviii + 334pp. 5⅜ x 8.   S311 Paperbound **$1.85**

INTERNAL CONSTITUTION OF THE EARTH, edited by Beno Gutenberg. Completely revised. Brought up-to-date, reset. Prepared for the National Research Council this is a complete & thorough coverage of such topics as earth origins, continent formation, nature & behavior of the earth's core, petrology of the crust, cooling forces in the core, seismic & earthquake material, gravity, elastic constants, strain characteristics and similar topics. "One is filled with admiration . . . a high standard . . . there is no reader who will not learn something from this book," London, Edinburgh, Dublin, Philosophic Magazine. Largest bibliography in print: 1127 classified items. Indexes. Tables of constants. 43 diagrams. 439pp. 6⅛ x 9¼.
S414 Paperbound **$2.45**

HYDROLOGY, edited by Oscar E. Meinzer. Prepared for the National Research Council. Detailed complete reference library on precipitation, evaporation, snow, snow surveying, glaciers, lakes, infiltration, soil moisture, ground water, runoff, drought, physical changes produced by water, hydrology of limestone terranes, etc. Practical in application, especially valuable for engineers. 24 experts have created "the most up-to-date, most complete treatment of the subject," AM. ASSOC. of PETROLEUM GEOLOGISTS. Bibliography. Index. 165 illustrations. xi + 712pp. 6⅛ x 9¼.   S191 Paperbound **$2.95**

Dover publishes books on art, music, philosophy, literature, languages, history, social sciences, psychology, handcrafts, orientalia, puzzles and entertainments, chess, pets and gardens, books explaining science, intermediate and higher mathematics, mathematical physics, engineering, biological sciences, earth sciences, classics of science, etc. Write to:

Dept. catrr.
Dover Publications, Inc.
180 Varick Street, N. Y. 14, N. Y.